My Weekly
2021 ANNUAL

FICTION

PAGE
108

PAGE
138

PAGE
162

CELEBRITY

FANCY THAT

HELPING HAND BAKES

BRAINBOOSTERS

/DC THOMSON
MEDIA

WORDS: SUSAN WATSON PICTURES: SHUTTERSTOCK, WENN

Magic Moments

Nadiya Hussain, who rocketed to fame when she won the *Great British Bake Off*, shares her best times…

Winning GBBO

Nadiya will never forget the moment her life changed forever, when she was announced as the winner of the *Great British Bake Off* in 2015.

"When I heard my name, I covered my face with my hands as I didn't want anyone to watch me cry. Mary and Paul hugged me and Mary told me I deserved to win, and that made me cry again!"

Kitchen Creations

"I discovered the magic of baking the first time I saw my Home Economics teacher mix flour, eggs and sugar and put them in the oven. My passion for baking was definitely sparked at that point.

"However I didn't really start baking seriously until I was 21 and got married and realised my husband loves cakes.

"I thought, 'Well, if he eats it, I'll make it!'"

Birthday Feast

December 25 is filled with magic moments for Nadiya as not only is it Christmas, it's also her birthday!

"My family come over to mine – there's about twenty-eight of us – and I'll cook everything.

"There are no words to describe the gluttony. There is so much food! It's a ridiculous amount but I love it as it's the one time of year that all of us have time off so we can all be together." ➔

Happy And Glorious!

Relive with us some of the most joyful, uplifting and memorable Royal moments in recent history...

A Right Royal Kiss

Kate and William announced their engagement in 2010 and there was much excitement leading up to their 2011 wedding. Over 36 million of us tuned in to watch. The best moment came as the happy couple stepped onto the Buckingham Palace balcony to share their first public kiss.

Happy Family!

The Duke and Duchess with their growing family:
Prince George Alexander Louis, born July 22, 2012.
Princess Charlotte Elizabeth Diana, born May 2, 2015.
Prince Louis Arthur Charles, born April 23, 2018.

One's A Bond Girl!

Having reigned for over 67 years, the Queen has had many important moments – some momentous such as her Coronation, others happy like sailing down the Thames to mark her Diamond Jubilee. But never has she made us smile more than when she entered into the spirit of the 2012 Olympics for her "skydiving mission" with Daniel Craig as James Bond!

Festive Romance

We all had an extra special Christmas present delivered in 2012 when, after a very rocky path to true love, *Downton Abbey*'s Matthew and Mary finally got it together. Matthew told his love, "You've lived your life. And I've lived mine. And now it's time we live them together."

There was snow, romantic declarations, the perfect kiss, and an engagement, all set against the classic *Downton* backdrop – surely the perfect romantic TV moment.

That Lake Scene

10 million viewers were gripped by the 1995 BBC version of Jane Austen's *Pride And Prejudice* – and that was before the infamous lake scene, which delighted viewers in episode four of the six part series.

A topless Poldark with his scythe pales in comparison to a decidedly damp Darcy fresh from a swim in the lake at Pemberley. It was the iconic TV moment that kicked off a national swoonathon... BBC period drama at its finest!

The Nation Watched...

Once in a while, there's an astonishing TV moment that brings us all together. Is your favourite here?

Who Shot JR?

In 1980, almost 22 million people tuned in to find out the answer to one of the biggest questions in TV history... who shot JR?

Dallas gave us the ultimate TV cliffhanger when oil magnate JR Ewing was shot by an unknown assailant. Having double-crossed and plotted against all the other characters on the show, almost everyone was a suspect.

On November 21, after weeks of fevered speculation, the shooter was finally revealed to be his mistress, Kristin Shepard.

The Audition

Britain's Got Talent has given us everything from a human ventriloquist dummy to an OAP break dancer. However every so often, in amongst all the craziness, a talent emerges that is breathtaking in its sheer perfection.

We all got tingles down our spine when in 2009, unassuming Susan Boyle from Bathgate broke out into an extraordinary rendition of *I Dreamed A Dream*, rendering the judging panel speechless. Reality TV at its absolute best, and still a YouTube sensation. (MW)

Kate Thompson

For The Love Of Lily

Taking out her anger on her husband's brother, little does the young war widow suspect the secrets he keeps…

Stratford, East London,
November 1944

Lily Button was locked in yet another furious row with her brother-in-law, Ronnie. "The trouble with you, Ronnie Button –"

"Ronald… My name's Ronald."

Lily rolled her eyes extravagantly.

"Well, excuse me. The trouble with you, *Ronald* Button, is that you're too uptight. You're a stuffed shirt, unlike…"

"….Arthur? That's what you wanted to say wasn't it?" he said crisply. "That I'm not half as much fun as Arthur."

"He wasn't afraid to get his hands dirty."

At the mention of her late husband and his brother's name, both their eyes strayed to the framed portrait over the mantel in the Button family home in Carpenters Road. Arthur's kind, blue eyes seemed to be imploring them to get along.

"Come on, you two, we're already fighting one war," pleaded May Button. "Arthur would've hated to see his two favourite people at loggerheads."

Ronald stood stiffly, fiddling with the cuff links on his starched white shirt.

"I'm sorry, Mum," he said. "I've got to go, I've a meeting in Whitehall."

"I thought you was on leave, son?"

"I've been called in."

In the photo Arthur's kind, blue eyes seemed to be imploring them to get along

"Meaning?" Ronald's face darkened.

Lily paused, aware she may well have gone too far this time.

"Oh, I see. You think I'm a coward because I'm not in uniform."

"Well, what exactly are you doing for the war effort?"

"You wouldn't understand."

"Because I'm a simple factory girl?" she said sarcastically. "Well, it was good enough for Arthur before he signed up."

He shot a last murderous look at Lily and swept from the tiny terrace, slamming the door so hard the sash windows rattled.

"He's a bit uptight at the moment, Lily love, go easy on him."

"When's he going back to that place, where is it again?"

"Bletchley Park. Tomorrow."

"Can't come soon enough. Sorry, May, I know he's your son but he's also a terrible snob. He looks down on me." ➡

Lily had grown up two doors down from the Button brothers and even as kids it was the same. With his permanently scabbed knees and striking blue eyes Arthur was the younger of the brothers and the street daredevil, who always had to go that bit faster and higher.

Ronald on the other hand was always at the library, or inside with his head in a book. Whenever Lily tried to talk him into coming out to play she'd got short shrift.

"He's a proper brain on him," was all anyone could say when his name was mentioned. "He's going places, that one."

Lily never paid him much attention, not when Arthur came knocking with one of his schemes.

She remembered the times he got her

stop them. The futility of his death cut savagely. A lovely young man, in the prime of his life. Nearly five years on, she was still no closer to making sense of it.

"Oh love," said May gently. "Don't let Ron get to you."

"It's not that. I just wish Arthur were still here. I know I'm not allowed to say that in wartime, keep calm and carry on and all that… but, oh God." She broke down. "I'm so lonely."

"I know you miss him, my darlin'," said her mother-in-law, softly. "We all do. And none more so than Ron. He adored his little brother. He was that proud of him when he married you – and when he went and signed up."

"Really?" Lily replied. "He's got a

The dreaded sound grew from a dull throbbing to a full throttle staccato

into trouble – when he persuaded her to play Knock Down Ginger, or the time he'd had to carry her home, blood gushing from her shin when he talked her into trying out his home-made kart down the slope into the canal. He had a charm that meant, somehow, she'd always say yes.

Lily couldn't recall when they had officially become a couple. They were always just Lily and Arthur, the street's childhood sweethearts, destined to marry.

She glanced at their wedding portrait. There was Arthur, puffed up with pride on the steps of the church and her, pretty as a picture in Belgium lace and orange blossom, gazing up at him.

Taken the day before hostilities were declared, but despite the shadow of war, it had been the happiest day of her life. How were any of them to know that he'd be dead less than nine months later?

The tears were on her before she could

funny way of showing it. He didn't even come to the wedding."

"He had important work on… And of course he struggled, seeing Arthur…"

"Seeing Arthur what?"

"Nothing, love. The point is, you may have lost a husband, but he's lost his little brother, and that ain't right either."

Lily sighed. "I'm sorry, May. You lost a son too, I'm being insensitive."

The factory hooter sounded.

"You best be off, love," said May. "Think about what I said."

Lily clocked on. Usually the clank and whirr rhythm of the conveyor belt soothed her fractured thoughts, but after her row with Ronald, she couldn't settle.

"You all right, Lil?" asked her best pal, Renee. "You've fused the machine twice this morning. Not that I care. It's so boring, packing these."

She held up a pot of Army camouflage cream. Since Yardley's had been requisitioned for the war effort, more often that not they found themselves packing aircraft components, rather than Lavender Water.

"Least we got the Yardley Christmas show to look forward to next month."

"Hmm."

The look of hurt on Ronald's face flashed through Lily's mind. She'd basically accused him of being a coward.

"And I get to walk naked all the way up the High Street," Renee went on.

"Yeah."

"Lily Button, you ain't listening to a word I'm saying!" Renee laughed.

"Oh I'm sorry, Renee." She sighed. She knew she owed Ronald an apology.

When the hooter sounded, Lily pulled out her compact. She applied a careful slick of the last bit of her Victory Red lipstick. Pulling off her turban, she combed out her wavy red hair.

Renee whistled under her breath.

"Move over, Betty Grable."

"Shut up," Lily laughed.

"Hope he's worth it," Renee called as she clocked out.

The number 25 seemed to take an age to get from East to West London and as the streets broadened into what she and Arthur had always dubbed Posh Land, she began to have serious doubts.

Why hadn't she just waited until Ronald got home, to apologise there? She didn't even know which office he was visiting…

And then she saw him, stepping outside a large white-stuccoed building chatting to a WREN.

"Ronnie!" She stood up to shout through the bus window. He looked up, surprised. "Sorry – Ronald I mean."

"Lily, what are you doing here?"

"Wait there," she called back. "I'm getting off the bus. I wanted to say…"

Her voice was drowned out by a sickeningly familiar spluttering.

Phut. Phut. Phut.

The sound rose up from the bowels of the earth, growing from a dull throbbing to a full throttle staccato.

A huge black rocket, with flames forking from the end was heading over the rooftops in the direction of Ronald's building.

Heart punching in her chest, she squeezed her eyes shut. *Please don't let him be hurt.*

The noise roared through her brain like a speedway motorbike.

Silence. The engine had cut out.

Where is it?" she gasped, opening her eyes. What she saw made the blood in her veins turn to ice. Terrifyingly, the rocket had changed course and was now slicing through the skies towards the bus.

"Lily!" Ronald yelled. "Get down."

She watched the scream freeze on his lips as a shadow passed over his face.

The air was thick with choking, acrid dust. Lily tried to move, then realised she couldn't, her legs were pinned down by the mangled remains of what looked like a bus door. All about her, muffled groans pierced the darkness.

Somewhere up above was sky. She ➡

seemed to be in a crater, with the wreckage of a double-decker bus partly on top of her.

"Help," she choked, but her voice was no more than a whisper.

The debris to the left of her started to shake and more dust streamed over her. The bus was precariously suspended half in, half out of the crater. One inch and the whole thing could come crashing down.

"I don't want to die," she whimpered.

A hand pushed through the wreckage, then a leg, followed by a face.

"Ronald!" she exclaimed.

"Lily!" he gasped. "Oh, thank God you're alive."

"I can't feel my legs."

"It's all right, it's all right," he soothed, taking her hands. "Heavy rescue are on their way. We'll get you out."'

"You shouldn't be here," she whispered. "This could come down at any moment."

"I'm not going anywhere."

He pulled a clean handkerchief from his pocket and gently wiped the dust from her eyelids.

"That better?" He smiled.

"Your shirt." She laughed, more from hysteria than anything. "It's ruined."

"Well, I am a stuffed shirt. You said the exact same thing yourself."

Her laughter gave way to a wracking cough. Her eyelids began to flicker.

"Lily! Lily…" he cried. "Stay with me."

"I'm cold, Ronald."

Hastily, he pulled off his jacket and wrapped it round her upper body.

"Please don't leave me. I'm scared."

"I'm right here with you," he soothed.

"I'm not going anywhere, I promise."

"Keep talking to me, Ronald," she whispered as she fell into unconsciousness.

So he did, as the minutes ticked into hours and the sound of banging and drilling got louder, he never left her side.

"You do get in some scrapes, Lily," he whispered. "Like the time you nearly ended up in the canal after that go-kart fell apart. Or the time, Arthur dared you to climb the factory walls. I thought my heart would never recover."

He looked at her beautiful pale face, the waxen fingers threaded through his.

"You've always had my heart though, Lily…"

Just as he voiced the words he'd kept locked in his heart for twenty-five years, the rescuers finally broke through.

It was a full three days before Lily regained consciousness in hospital and she couldn't remember a thing about what had happened. May and Renee told her how it had taken a team of rescuers four hours to free her from the wreckage, but it was the news of Ronald's role which shocked her the most.

"He sat with you all that time, refused to leave, even when rescuers told him that his life was in danger," said May. "ARP have put his name forward for a civilian bravery award."

Lily watched in fascination as Ronald's face coloured and his fingers fiddled with his cufflinks. In that moment, she suddenly saw with a piercing clarity. Ronald wasn't rude or uptight. He was simply shy.

She attempted to sit up but gasped as a stabbing pain gripped her side. Alarm flashed over his face.

"Careful, Lily. I don't think there's a rib you haven't broken."

Gently he plumped her pillows and motioned to a nurse for more water.

"I'll fetch it," said May. "These poor nurses are overworked enough as it is. Come on, Renee, you can help me."

"Ronald," Lily said softly when they were alone, resting her fingers on his.

"Ronnie," he replied and she smiled.

"I don't know how I'll ever truly be able to repay you for what you did."

"Just tell me why you were on a bus outside my work?" he asked.

"I came to say sorry – for accusing you

When May and Renee returned to the bedside, May only had to take one look at both of their faces to see what had passed between them.

Gently, she placed the water jug on the bedside table.

"Son, you look shattered. You've barely left this girl's bedside for the past three days. You get off home and have a rest. Take Renee with you."

Ronald knew better than to argue with his mum. He shot a last lingering look at the woman he'd loved all his life, certain she would never want to see him again.

"Bye, Lily," he said.

"Bye, Ronnie. And thanks again."

When they were out of earshot, May sat down.

May took one look at their faces and saw what had passed between them

of being a coward." Shame coursed through her and she began to cry.

Ronald pulled out his handkerchief.

"Please don't cry, Lily. I'm the idiot. All those times I was rude to you when we were growing up. No wonder you think I'm a perfect prig."

Gently, he wiped her eyelids. The action triggered a memory and Lily gasped. A flashback of the rocket attack roared into her mind and she gripped the sides of the hospital bed as the memories flooded back.

Ronnie breaking through the debris, holding her hand, and promising never to let go… Ronnie talking about how he used to hide in the library so he didn't have to see her, how he couldn't face coming to the wedding because…

"You're in love with me?" she gasped.

Ronnie hung his head and nodded.

"Hopelessly. I always have been, Lily."

"Now you see why I told you to go easy on him. I always say that both my boys clapped eyes on your beautiful red hair and fell in love instantly.

"But I always knew it would be my youngest who'd win your heart. Arthur could charm the birds out the sky."

"I thought Ronald was a stick in the mud," Lily murmured, filled with guilt.

"Heads are always turned by the dashing ones." May nodded wisely.

"Poor Ronald." Lily sighed. "Is that why he never got a sweetheart?"

"No one could ever match up to you."

"So what now? Do I just pretend it never happened?"

May looked at her with a knowing smile.

"Oh, you could do a lot worse."

Lily's eyes opened wide.

"Are you saying what I think you're saying? What about Arthur?"

"Arthur loved you two more than ➡

any other people in this whole world. To see you find some happiness amid this dreadful war would fill his heart with joy."

She stood up to leave and touched her daughter-in-law's hand.

"Trust me, I know I'm right."

It was Christmas Eve when Lily was finally discharged back to Carpenters Road. The snow was falling thickly on the cobbles and the East End was blanketed under a crisp white carpet.

Ronald and May helped Lily as she stepped carefully out the taxi Ronald had splurged on to get her home safely.

"Welcome home, love," said May, pushing open the door to the warmth of the tiny terrace.

"Can I just wait here a moment?" said Lily. "I've been cooped up for so long, I've forgotten what fresh air feels like."

She turned and looked up at Ronald,

"No, it's all right. When will you be going back to Bletchley?"

"Boxing Day."

"In that case, I think I'd rather spend the evening here at home, with you."

Ronald stared down at her and she felt her heart pick up speed.

"Can I ask you something?"

"Anything, Lily," he murmured.

Do you believe in heaven? Do you think Arthur's up there now watching us?"

Ronald shrugged and they both looked up at the starry vault overhead.

"The mathematician in me says no, but…" His voice trailed off as a shooting star blazed over the factory rooftops.

"Some things you can't explain."

They turned back to one another and as she gazed up into his hopeful eyes, Lily felt her heart expand with love. Ronald would never replace Arthur, nor would he want to, but right now she felt that their

"The mathematician in me says no, but some things you can't explain…"

her breath billowing like smoke. Overhead, the inky sky was filled with a canopy of twinkling stars.

"This is our sixth Christmas at war," she murmured.

"And our fifth without Arthur," he replied sombrely.

With his collars pulled up and his hair swept back with brilliantine, she suddenly noticed his eyes. They were sapphire blue, cut like gemstones. She'd never noticed that, but then it was funny what she saw now her own eyes had been opened.

In the distance, laughter and applause echoed from the factory.

Do you want me to take you to the Yardley Christmas show?" he asked.

She smiled and shook her head.

being together was the only way to make sense of their losses.

"And what would the mathematician say the chances are of you kissing me?" she asked cheekily.

Ronald smiled now, a huge soppy grin that lit up his whole face.

"Every chance." He drew Lily into his arms and held her face in his hands as delicately as if she were made of china.

"I've loved you for all of my life, Lily," he murmured. "And hoping that you could maybe love me back one day, is a kind of a miracle."

"Christmas is a time for miracles," she replied softly.

And under the starry Stratford sky, Ronald and Lily kissed at last. ⓂⓌ

"I Love To Write"

Journalist turned author Kate Thompson picks out five highlights from her amazing career...

I didn't excel at school and came out with woeful exam results. I think hormones may have played a part! The only thing I had any confidence in was writing. I always had my nose in a book and loved to write creative stories. My English teacher was wonderful and it's thanks to her that I pursued a career in journalism.

Back then, the only route in was to take a postgraduate National Council for Training Journalists (NCTJ) certificate. They only accepted two candidates not degree-educated. So I worked my hardest, building up a portfolio of stories from unpaid work experience on local papers. I was extremely nervous at interview but must have said something right as they offered me a place.

Getting my first paid journalism job at Fleet Street News Agency when I was 21 was a fantastic moment. The hours were deadly and the pay derisory, but it taught me valuable lessons about hard work, professionalism, how to talk to people and encourage them to open up to you. Being a journalist means you speak with people encountering the very best and worst moments of their life. I have concluded that a little compassion goes a long way.

By 2006, I was working as Deputy Editor for Pick Me Up! magazine where I won

Best Real Life Story award, handed over by comedian Jimmy Carr. The story was about a young girl from the Philippines who'd had both legs amputated. Her family had to carry her everywhere as there was no access to medical care or prosthetics. It was so gratifying to highlight her plight and Jimmy Carr was really lovely!

Getting my first book deal for _Secrets Of The Singer Girls_ with Pan Macmillan in 2014 was beyond anything I can begin to describe. My husband heard me put the phone down and burst into tears. He rushed in to find out what was wrong. We celebrated with my mum and dad and copious fizz. Having come out of school with one GCSE it was a wonderful moment to share with my long-suffering parents.

Every time I get a letter or email from a reader saying what joy my books bring them, I feel ridiculously grateful and honoured. There's no better way to earn a living than by writing stories.

Kate Thompson is author of a number of East End based wartime novels, including _Secrets Of The Homefront Girls_ and _Lavender Girls_, published by Hodder & Stoughton.

Deck The Halls...

Well-worn family traditions can be the source of as much strife as brash new ideas if you ask me!

By Valerie Bowes

You wouldn't believe 365 days could possibly go so quickly, but here it is again. Christmas.

Those fairy lights make the room look cheerful, don't they? But I reckon the rest of the things are looking distinctly the worse for wear.

The trouble is, those decorations aren't simply coloured paper and tarnished tinsel. They're memories. That wishy-washy pink bell was a rich crimson when Jim and Karen bought it for Tanya's first Christmas, and now she's fourteen.

round for Christmas dinner. And why Jim and Karen had a blazing great row about it last night.

"Why's it always got to be us?" she demanded. "You want a traditional Christmas with all the trimmings, but who does it all? And your Auntie Peg will be embarrassing and Margery and Derek'll bring another bottle of that ghastly Vin Duty-Free…"

Personally, I think she was just feeling rather tired and emotional after Jim had commented that the pudding she'd made back in November was looking a bit dry.

Those decorations aren't simply paper and tarnished tinsel. They're memories

And Tanya and Kevin made those paperchains when she was seven and he was five. Christmas just wouldn't be Christmas without them.

Still, the tree's way past its sell-by date, don't you think? Karen insisted on this artificial job a couple of Christmases after they were married. She was tired of vacuuming up pine needles, but Jim wasn't happy. *Not traditional,* he said.

He's a great one for tradition. That's why we always have the whole family

He got round her – told her she makes the best Christmas dinner ever. But I could tell she thought he was right about that pudding, because she doused it in whisky and left it to soak until this morning.

Jim's very pleased with his power planer. None too subtle of her, though, if you ask me. She's been on at him to do ➡

something about the kitchen for ages.

He wasn't that subtle, either, come to think of it. Black silk and lace! Really. She went quite pink.

Tanya and Kevin had so many things to open, I don't think they knew where to start, but Tanya seemed pleased with her new iPhone and Kevin was definitely thrilled with that computer game.

We always watch The Queen, but then there's usually one of these blockbuster films they put on especially for the season of Peace and Goodwill, all guns and bombs and people going *Arghhh!* I can see Tanya's music and Kevin's computer game fitting in a treat, can't you?

Oh, there's the doorbell. I don't know what they're going to make of our Tanya. The new black nail varnish

dancing, and Auntie Peg's shown them some wicked moves. There, look – now they've got me at it.

The others crowded into the kitchen to have a good old-fashioned natter. Someone started the reminiscences going and they've been at it full blast ever since. You should've heard the shrieks of laughter. Kevin even asked them to keep the noise down.

Someone started the reminiscing. You should've heard the shrieks of laughter

and pelmet skirt are going to come as a bit of a shock. Nearly frightened the life out of me when I first saw her, I can tell you.

Kevin said she looked wicked. That was a bit unkind of him, I thought, because she's the same sweet Tanya underneath the make-up.

My mistake. "Wicked" must be praise of the highest order, because he said the same to his mum after their Christmas dinner and he'd had at least two helpings of everything that was on the table.

And everybody thought it was the best pudding ever!

Maybe it was, because it's been a really great Christmas Day. Grandpa, of all people, turned out to be a whizz at Kevin's new computer game, so he and Kevin spent the afternoon playing with it. Tanya and her cousins have been

Oh, right. Here we go. There's Jim, same as every year, raising his glass to me with a wink. But now he's promising to get a proper tree, pine needles and all.

Right! It had better not be the pudding talking, because I'm holding him to it. I've been on the top of his tree ever since he was a little lad – but there's tradition and then there's tat. Unless he gets me a new one, he can find another fairy.

So there you are. And a very Merry Christmas to you all! **MW**

MY MAGIC MOMENT...

The first time I went snorkelling was breathtaking in more ways than one. From swimming in an opaque, uninteresting sea to a place of life and colour – all in the blink of a mask.

Codeword

**Each letter of the alphabet has been replaced by a number.
The numbers for the first name of our chosen celebrity are given.
Complete the puzzle to find out which two nationalities make up
Natalie Portman's dual citizenship?**

Turn To
Page 155 For
Solutions

The Girl In The Red Shoes

A speed dating Secret Santa night? Heaven for some, hell for anyone like Evie still smarting from a break-up...

By Judy Jarvie

Mel picked a Christmas winner event with this one! This dating night is a festive showstopper!"

Jake Smith, True Love Ways dating agency's latest recruit, brimmed with the enthusiasm of a recent appointee unfazed by too-regular marketing gimmicks. It would soon pass.

Evie Pringle forced on a smile and agreed. Hopefully her faked joy and the surrounding festive décor of their wine bar-slash-brasserie venue would fool everybody that she was feeling the Christmas cheer that had been snuffed out of her in the last few weeks.

"Well – you're certainly dressed for

living the dream. Bringing couples together – inspiring new love. Like Cupid but with corporate benefits and a pension scheme."

Jake reminded Evie of an upbeat Mark Darcy from the first Bridget Jones movie – only with no lucrative career as a barrister as a counterpoint to his gauche ways or Christmas outfit affliction.

Evie smiled through her pain. The red stilettos she'd been forced to wear for her elf costume were two sizes too small. She also had to repeatedly tug down her dress in order to remain decent.

"Mel's always been obsessed by Christmas, Jake. Combining speed dating with a Secret Santa theme is right up her street. It's a great idea for a charity fundraiser," she said, feeling like a closet

Jake winked at her and his flashing braces suddenly upped tempo

the occasion, Jake!" she remarked.

Jake's outfit put the crass in Christmas. His tie featured dancing reindeer with glow-in-the-dark noses. The addition of flashing braces was a fashion police offence too far. Nobody had warned her to bring sunglasses for her eye health either.

"You enjoying my old job then, Jake?"

He grinned. "Won the job lottery; I'm

Scrooge as this was her own private hell.

It felt as if her hospitable smile was stuck on with glitter glue – the kind she'd used on Christmas cards with the kids in her new job in the nursery. She'd come as a helper tonight for Mel. Though right now, Christmas celebrations were the last thing she needed...

"We'll have a dance later if you're up

for it, Evie? Fancy a boogie to Shakin' Stevens?" Jake asked with a wink she'd rather not have witnessed. Especially as his flashing braces suddenly upped tempo.

Jake fiddled with the battery. At least, she hoped that's what he was doing in his pocket. It seemed to rectify the problem.

"Not in these shoes, Jake, but thanks. I wouldn't want to over-stimulate your battery either." Evie edged away. She wouldn't be dancing. Or encouraging Jake's flash dance aspirations.

In fact, as soon as she could get tonight over with, she'd disappear to her flat – a home that still didn't have a Christmas tree up because she couldn't find it in her to decorate it. Given the chance, she'd be out of Maddison's Brasserie and Wine Bar like Santa with a fixed penalty late delivery clause and a parking ticket.

This Christmas hadn't brought her any of the good things she'd hoped for.

Her new job as a qualified nursery teacher had coincided with Nathan ➤

reaching a personal epiphany and moving out. Like a Christmas cracker that had exploded in her face without warning, full of painful, unexpected life changes. He'd met somebody else at work at the call centre; it was serious, apparently.

So what if he'd just detonated her future?

So their families wouldn't be joining up for the planned big Christmas dinner at the new flat. She'd spent the last week rearranging the mortgage into her sole name. Evie planned to hand the enormous turkey she'd pre-ordered in to the local homeless shelter to make good use of it.

Only a few months ago she'd been engaged, happy, on the verge of a new career. All good things ahead. Now she was dreading a solo Christmas and ghosts of might-have-beens.

"I plan to seek you out with mistletoe," Jake called after her.

Evie vowed to keep a low profile. Even if it meant hiding behind the Christmas tree or doing sniper moves to escape him.

"Find some girls who like men in flashing trousers. If you can!" she muttered, walking away, as her patience shattered like a glass bauble on the pavement.

The unmistakable sultry tones of *Santa Baby* crooned as flashing lights pulsed a turbo Ibiza beat. David Blake did not want to be here.

He wouldn't have been here; had he not had his arm twisted at work.

Still, as Homeless SOS Rescue were set to receive a generous cheque from this event, as support worker manager he'd had to oblige. Step into the breach. Say yes, like a mug.

And act as if Speed Dating Secret Santa was something sane people chose to do on a Friday night.

So far, the mingling attendees looked like an explosion in a Christmas shop. One woman wore a sizeable pair of antlers with Lederhosen hot pants that made him do a double-take. There were a couple of snowmen, and a giant, skinny male elf who'd have done Will Ferrell's Buddy proud.

There were angels and a clutch of shepherds. Someone was actually dressed as a star, draped in more bling than Elton John's party piano.

David was ready for the fastest U-turn in history but Jodie's iron grip kept him there as their eyes locked.

"You're here for me, remember? Callum is coming, this is my big chance. Think I've spotted him. Tall snowman at one o'clock. The one with his carrot nose around his neck." His sister glared at him from under her jaunty, sexy Christmas pudding hat. "You promised you would help me. *And* you need to be here for work."

"Some things are just asking too much, Jo. It's so not my scene."

"You could surprise yourself, enter into the Christmas spirit. It won't hurt to crack a smile. Ruthie was years ago; you can't pine forever. She has twins now and lives in France. You need to get over it."

"I don't tend to want to smile much when I'm made to wear fancy dress that includes bells and pointy shoes."

Much to his chagrin Jodie laughed.

"But you make a great Santa, Dave. Don't let anybody tell you different. Go on – give us a *ho, ho, ho!*"

"Don't push me, sister."

The costume had been one lent to Jodie by a friend. It was the kind of long-cloaked costume that had probably made its debut at a Sunday School party in the 1920s. Worse still, its hem featured jingle bells. He actually smelled of mothballs; that at least should keep the women away.

He still couldn't believe he was wearing it. Or doing this.

"Lighten up, brother!"

"Let me go home, then! I've heard there's a good tin of paint I could be watching dry there."

As if by Christmas magic, an attractive elf with stunning, blonde curls and over-large elf ears appeared with a tray of dubious drinks.

"X-rated Egg Nog or Virgin Mary Mulled Wine? What's your poison, Santa?"

"I'll pass, thanks – I'm driving. The reindeer get antsy if I go rogue," David answered while Jodie grabbed a glass of Egg Nog and glugged.

"Steady with the Egg Nog," whispered the enchanting blue-eyed Elf to his sister.

Pud and your friend as Jingle Bells Sober Santa. We've so many Santas, I'm struggling for unique names for badges."

"Sober Santa. My life's now complete," David answered. Again she stared and their gazes held. He tried to reply but failed. And how had his tongue got glued to the top of his mouth? He blamed the awful punch.

The glacier-blue eyes had him riveted. Or was it the shapely figure in a red and green elf dress?

One glance down at the red stilettos, and he was suddenly very warm in his North Pole cloak.

Elf woman was saying, "Anyway. Feel free to mingle. Then, when Angel Gabriella (that's Mel, our boss) rings the bell, take a seat and it's time for speed-dating kick-off! There are forms to fill on the table. All self-explanatory. And it's for charity." The elf stared again. "Good luck to you both."

A bell sounded and someone began giving loud directions through a mic.

Dave murmured softly, "Is now a

"The Virgin Mary Mulled Wine is non-alcoholic. The reindeer won't mind"

"It's a cross between winter spiced paint stripper and wallpaper paste! Small sips! As for you…" He found her gaze caused something inside him to warm up nicely. Like a night in front of a log fire – very appealing. "Virgin Mulled Wine is non-alcoholic. The reindeer won't mind."

"I'll tell Rudolph."

Their gazes tangoed.

"Warning; it still tastes vile however."

He stared at the woman and found he liked her. He didn't quite know why. And she looked at him strangely – maybe he was staring? She eyeballed Jodie and her cheeks were flushed.

"I'll put you down as Sexy Christmas

good time to go next door and watch live football instead?"

"If you want total honesty, I'd rather be in there myself," Elf answered.

Jodie jabbed him in the ribs.

"We'll find your jingle bells if it kills us!"

Elf woman laughed. She had lovely white teeth, he noticed.

"Are you taking part?" he asked but she was already drifting, dealing with someone else. Why had he asked that? What was with him? He blamed the costume, making him go places he'd usually steer clear of.

"Spotted a Christmas cracker you'd like to pull?" Jodie teased. "It's a miracle."

David suddenly felt hot. And not just ➔

from the velvet Santa garb. As if he'd just been given brandy and set alight.

He sent her a last smile that she caught and smiled back. Then shouted, "Your attendance here will help a lot of worthy people. Homelessness SOS Rescue. Nice to put money where it counts."

David wanted to say, *I know, I work there.* But Jodie was pulling him and pushing another drink into his hand and a large jovial Santa was singing The Pogues too loudly and he wasn't able to linger with the mystery Elf Girl with the name badge that, intriguingly, read *Christmas Evie.*

Sensing Jake moving in to talk again, Evie seized her moment to move into one of the darker corners of the room. Not only because her feet were now mincemeat. Jake's upbeat pursuit had become cloying.

A few times he laughed openly, throwing his head back. He then removed his beard and hood – definitely handsome. At one point a woman held out mistletoe and he obliged with a peck on her cheek.

A sting of annoyance stabbed inside Evie at the sight.

"So much for wanting to escape it! Even Santa lies when he chooses to!"

Evie knew she'd felt a spark when they'd talked. That rarely happened – not since she'd dated Nathan anyway. A kindred dislike of their situation had been voiced and now she felt betrayed. As if Santa had delivered something unwanted.

Evie pressed her temples, feet and head throbbing equally. She wanted to go home.

With mounting horror she watched a familiar figure enter the wine bar and brasserie door, cool night air sweeping in to chill her through. Nathan – her ex-

Gravity won. The tree fell in a crash of broken baubles and mangled lights

Nor could she handle the smiling. The dire fake grins – was a breather too much to ask? The giant Christmas tree at the back of the room offered a perfect sanctuary spot. Like a well-timed gift.

"Thank you, Santa, whoever you are!" Evie silently stepped behind it.

In her hiding place behind the towering silver-lit tree, Evie hoped to surreptitiously prize off the painful footwear, but it was difficult in the cramped space.

She heard the babble of speed dating small talk as she gently tried to remove her shoes with foot force alone, but failed.

The dark-browed, hunky Santa with the stark grey eyes and long cloak was close by. He'd come in morose, reluctant – in sharp contrast to his jolly Christmas pud companion, but now he seemed at ease.

Nathan – dressed smartly in his favourite suit jacket, one she'd once helped him choose – stood with a perky brunette holding his arm, sporting a sleek shiny bob.

Evie's heart hammered a tattoo as she hoped she was dreaming this. Yet she knew that nightmares didn't happen with eyes open, and she'd just been personally delivered her worst Christmas gift.

Evie's gasp must have been audible as a nearby woman turned in surprise, just as the tree teetered and wobbled. Panicked, Evie tried to crouch, tucking herself deeper into the corner, yet only succeeded in knocking the tree which wobbled again.

Lights flickered. The tree toppled. Evie grabbed without effect and gravity won. The tree fell in a loud crash of broken baubles and mangled lights – a distorted centrepiece that was the antithesis of a bright, hope-filled Christmas.

With immaculate timing, her shoe, finally dislodged, flew across the polished floor like a sparkling missile and Evie, losing her balance, toppled head first among the tree branches.

Nathan and his girlfriend stood waiting, watching her humiliation. Speed dating participants moved to help, one retrieving her shoe. Sober Santa stood nearby.

As soon as Evie could stand she ran, sobbing, for the nearest exit. Christmas would never again be joy-filled – instead it was packed with reined-in tears, echoing with gasps of pity. Hot shame, and a cold heart turned to sharp ice.

D avid found her; shivering, at the fire exist. Her mascara was smudged, wet tear tracks evident – and she was still wearing one sparkling red shoe.

He handed her the other, unnerved at his boldness with a woman he didn't know, but he knew the signs.

He worked with people at their low points. He knew vulnerability. Straight-talking was the best gift you could give.

"OK there?"

Evie sniffed and he worried that she'd begin to cry again.

"Been better," she mumbled with a sideways glance.

"Mel told me. For what it's worth, I hope he has sleepless nights. He deserves the big wake-up call."

"Nathan? He didn't do anything. I knocked over the tree all on my own."

"He came out celebrating, strutting, showing off his new woman. He's plenty to feel bad about, Evie."

"I don't even know your name."

"It's Dave Blake. We got three grand, and I heard it was you who suggested us as nominated charity. We're very grateful, which means I owe you too.

"Anyway, I just wondered if you fancy coming to out our Night Kitchen some time over Christmas. We need volunteers as we get a lot of donations – shame not to make the most of them."

She smiled weakly. "I think I may be a liability at the moment."

"Listen. Tree vandalism is nothing. My sister's in there snogging a six foot snowman." He paused. "I can show you plenty of people who don't think smashing a Christmas tree is a bad night. You might not feel up for the shebang this year – but doesn't mean you can't lighten the load for others… I'm on shift that night, too. I'll keep you right."

Evie took her shoe and smiled.

"I'm game if you are. Got any use for a large Marks and Sparks turkey crown? Feeds twelve, comes with a bonus apprentice volunteer."

Sober Santa smiled.

"Now you're talking, Christmas Evie." Ⓜ

MY MAGIC MOMENT…

My magical writing moment has to be seeing my first My Weekly Pocket Novel on a shelf at my local shop! I've written five now and every "shelfie moment" is a magical thrill!

Celebration Time

We remember a special party for My Weekly's Helping Hand Appeal where the readers raised over £1 million!

The My Weekly Helping Hand Appeal has raised over £1 million since it started 20 years ago, starting off in 1999 as a campaign to send shoeboxes to Romania, followed by our amazing

Party Tiffin

Ingredients (Makes 16)

- ◆ **250g pack butter**
- ◆ **75g golden syrup**
- ◆ **2 x 125g packs Iced Ring biscuits**
- ◆ **185g pack pink wafers, finely chopped**
- ◆ **150g glacé cherries, chopped**
- ◆ **75g mini marshmallows**
- ◆ **2 x 150g bars white chocolate, broken into pieces**
- ◆ **Sprinkles to decorate**

1 Line a 25cm square cake tin with 2 layers of cling-film so that it overhangs the tin edge. Gently melt 190g butter with the syrup. Leave to cool for 10min.

2 Meanwhile, reserve 16 ring biscuits for decoration, crush the rest and place in a bowl. Mix in the wafers, cherries and mini marshmallows.

3 Pour over the cooled syrup and mix well. Pile into the prepared tin, press down well and chill for 30min.

4 Put the chocolate in a heatproof bowl. Add the remaining butter and place over a saucepan of barely simmering water to melt. Mix well to make a fudgy paste and spread over the biscuit base. Decorate with reserved ring biscuits and sprinkles. Chill for at least 2hrs.

5 Use the cling-film to help lift the tiffin from the tin. Peel away, and cut into 16 pieces to serve. **➜ P57**

readers raising this fantastic sum! This money has helped to feed children in countries around the world, in partnership with Mary's Meals enabling millions of youngsters to attend school. Hurrah!

RECIPE AND FOOD STYLING: KATHRYN HAWKINS PHOTOGRAPHY: STUART MACGREGOR

A Parting Gift

Penelope, the sweet old lady in the herb garden,
taught me so much in such a short time...

By Lydia Jones

Are you all right?"
A Jack-in-a-box would be slower to start than me.

"Sorry – I didn't mean to scare you." A wizened conker-face peers out from beneath a broad hat. "The herb garden doesn't get many visitors nowadays – they all go up to the Hall to the dig."

"I – just wanted to be alone."
Immediately I wish I'd put it less personally.

"Ah." She doesn't pry; I'm grateful.

"I've been walking here for weeks – I didn't realise it was a herb garden."

"Used to be." She looks sad. "it's all neglected since my husband died, but I try my best to keep it going."

"Thanks for walking the dog, love," Mum says later.

"No problem. I like it – it gives me exercise and time to – think."

"You're too much alone, Becca. Ever since –"

"It's OK, Mum – you can mention it. Since Jake decided to disappear off travelling, instead of moving in with me, you mean."

I hate being so bitter. Especially when Mum flinches.

I watch her garnering patience and composing her features.

"Well, why don't you contact your old friends now you're back? It would do you good to see people."

"Mmm. Maybe."

"Don't look so shocked." She chuckles. "Your generation didn't invent it"

"You're the gardener here, then?"

"I'm Penelope."

If it were possible, the furrowed face crinkles further as she smiles.

"Becca," I supply. "Penelope – can you solve something for me? I wondered why it says *Heart* on that bed of plants."

She grins. "Herbs are grouped according to how they help."

I scowl sceptically at what looks like a patch of weeds. "Are they for physical or emotional heart problems?"

"Both," she says, as if she can see through me to the mess inside.

But I don't. I return to the herb garden and self-pitying solitude. I'm not proud of myself.

Penelope's tended plants bring back memories of the plans I made so lovingly with Jake: a little house with flowers and a vegetable patch.

I'm sobbing, so I don't hear her approaching.

"Cry it out, sweetheart. The man was a complete fool."

"How did you know it was a man?"

"It always is. As for being a fool, that's easy – he let you go, didn't he?"

I can't help but smile at her deductions. "That's better. Now come along and help me weed the wound remedies. Calendula and Lavender.

"They will heal, you know," she continues conversationally. "The wounds inside, I mean. I gave my heart to a man in 1954." She chuckles. "And my other bits besides."

"Penelope!"

"Don't look so shocked. Your generation didn't invent it, you know."

"What happened?"

"Changed his mind, didn't he? I thought I was ruined forever but then I met John and everything began again."

"How did you know you could trust him – that he was the one?"

"Just the touch of a hand." Her gaze is decades away. "He helped me down from a train, and there – it felt as if my skin was on fire."

Helping Penelope, I begin in some indefinable way to feel better, reconnected to a future. We work most days. So I'm surprised when I enter the garden to find not Penelope, but a blond man pottering among the herb beds.

"Hello there." He has cerulean eyes. "News travels fast."

"News?" I repeat, puzzled.

"The chalice unearthed here – in the Nerves plot."

"Huh?"

"Sorry." He smiles. "I'm so fascinated with the find, I forget myself. I'm Luke – from the dig up at the Hall. The gardener

found the chalice earlier today."

"Gardener?"

Shut up, Becca! You sound like a parrot, for goodness' sake.

"Found it this morning. Funny, he said he hadn't been here for ages. Nobody has – not since old Penelope died."

"She *died?*"

Panic pricks inside my chest.

"I only met her once – lovely lady. She said she pottered here because it was her husband's favourite place."

"John."

"You knew him? Gardener here for fifty years. Keeping the garden going was her tribute to him, I suppose."

"So when did she die?"

I can feel the strangest idea forming.

He screws up features I realise suddenly are more than a smidgen handsome.

"Oooh, it was last year sometime."

"Could I – see the chalice?" I ask to buy myself composure time.

Luke reaches into our most recently weeded bed and hands me the soil-smeared chalice. As I take it, his fingertips brush mine and it is as if my skin is on fire.

I stroke Penelope's parting gift, hoping she can see the look Luke and I share. **Ⓜ**

MY MAGIC MOMENT...

It was in Italy. I was poolside; my daughter and husband were playing and laughing on the villa patio. In that moment I was so grateful we were happy and together in such a beautiful place.

Sigrid's Spell

After three sons, she longed for a daughter… but how would her husband react if her rituals worked?

By Valerie Bowes

"This time it will be a girl!"

Sigrid smoothed the hard roundness of her belly with a small, serene smile. There was a certainty in her voice that her friend, Gudrun, did not like. It didn't pay to be too certain about anything in this world. It only paved the path of disappointment.

"If hope will bring it about, then I shall have a son next time," she said tartly.

Sigrid laid her hand on Gudrun's arm and squeezed it in sympathy.

"You'll have another son one day, Gudrun. He won't replace Svein, but he will bring you joy."

"Bring Ragnar joy, you mean." Gudrun dashed the tear from her cheek and sniffed. "I'm quite happy with my girls, but every man wants a son. Had it been Aud or Marget who died, he would have grieved, but the loss of his boy has hit him hard."

"Children are so fragile, it sometimes surprises me that any of them survive." Sigrid sighed. "And sons most of all. I found Oddi in with the pigs the other day."

Gudrun laughed. "Did he smell like a midden when he came out?"

"He did, but that wasn't the problem. The old sow has piglings."

She didn't need to say more. Everyone, even a six-year-old, knew better than to get near a sow with young.

Gudrun's hand went to her mouth.

"What was he thinking of?"

"He dropped his bannock," Sigrid said, and couldn't help laughing. "Thank goodness I heard him shouting at the sow to leave it and pulled him out just in time."

"I'll warrant he set up a bawling to match the pigs!" Gudrun marvelled.

"They probably heard him in Hoy!" Sigrid said. "I told him his father would give him a skelping for being so foolish, but all Thorkell did was brush him round the ear and say he was a brave lad and that he'd take him boar-hunting in Sutherland when he was old enough to hold a spear. And then he told me to give the boy another bannock!"

Gudrun ceased her spinning.

"Well, but what makes you so sure the child will be a girl? After Einar, Oddi and Jon, your man must be expecting to have another fine lad to take hunting for boar and wolf and deer, and fishing for the silver darlings."

"All my lads I've carried low." Sigrid cradled her belly and teased another handful of wool from the heap. "This one is high. I didn't have the sickness so much before, either. This time, I was afraid I'd vomit the child up. Besides…" ➡

"I didn't have the sickness much before. This time I feared I'd vomit the child up"

She bent her head over the distaff, making very busy with the handful of wool.

"Besides?" Gudrun queried.

"And besides, I can't fancy meat. Fish or vegetables are the only things I can stomach since I first began to show."

Every man wanted his first-born to be a son. When they were first wed, Sigrid was determined that she would give Thorkell his heart's desire. Her mother had told her to lay a knife under the mattress and a roasted onion beneath her pillow. She had made sure her head faced north, even though it meant sleeping the other way around and Thorkell was mystified as to why she wanted it that way. She'd made sure she slept on Thorkell's left, and she'd eaten mutton

That evening, she dished out bowls of mutton stew to her husband and sons, then slid a fish onto her own plate with a helping of boiled sea kale. Thorkell looked at it with distaste and pointed with his wooden spoon.

"What's this? Not again? Hardly enough to keep a bird alive. Are you sick, Sigrid?"

She shook her head. "It's what I fancy."

Thorkell knew pregnant women have their odd desires. His own mother told him once she'd been afraid she'd give birth to a sheep, she craved mutton so. All the same, he frowned at the fish as if it was personally responsible for being on Sigrid's plate.

"You're sure you're not sickening for something? Or is it just the bairn making you queasy?"

Please, not yet. He's only eight winters old. Let him be my boy a little longer...

and cheese with a ravenous appetite.

It had worked. Einar was born within the year, a lustily-yelling son. Thorkell had taken him on his knee and announced with pride that he named him Einar, after his own father.

Then came Oddi, named after hers, and Jon, for Thorkell's brother. If she had a daughter, Sigrid thought as her fingers twirled the distaff with the ease of long practice, she would ask Thorkell if she might be named Elin.

The knife was no longer under the mattress. After Jon, she had taken it away. She'd told Thorkell she wanted to change back to sleeping with her head towards the south. He had sighed over the whims of women, but made no objection. And she made sure they made love at the full of the moon. She'd eaten only fish and vegetables. She'd done everything she could to make a girl.

"It's perfectly normal," she snapped at him. "Get on with your dinner. And eat up those bits, Einar. Do you think we can waste good food?"

"They're only gristle," Einar said. "You know I don't like gristle."

"Eat! It's good for you," Thorkell said. "You won't have to be so dainty when you go to Wyre."

Sigrid's breath caught in her throat. She'd known this day would come, ever since the midwife had laid Einar on her breast, but not yet.

Please, not yet. He's only eight winters old. Let him be my boy for a little longer.

Einar's spoon stopped half-way to his mouth. His eyes were round and very big.

"Wyre?" he said.

Sigrid could hear the faintest quaver in his voice and her heart ached.

Thorkell had been waiting for such an opportunity to tell them the good news.

"You are to go as foster-son to Kolbein Hruga." He beamed around at his family. "It is a great honour."

"And me?" Oddi said, eagerness shining from him like a candle.

"Later, my son."

"Why not now? Why can't I go with Einar to Wyre?"

Thorkell broke off a piece of bannock to dip in the savoury gravy.

"In two winters' time, you'll be of an age and I have a chieftain of Sutherland in my eye for you. Be a good lad and do as you're bid and you'll have as good a foster-father as your brother."

Thank God Jon hadn't yet reached his fourth winter. Sigrid helped her youngest son deal with a tough piece of meat while she prayed even more fervently that the child in her womb would be a maid.

When Thorkell first told her, several moons ago, of his hope that Kolbein would agree to take Einar, she had tried to make him think again.

"Must our sons be fostered? Not every boy is. Even our Earl's father kept him at home and it's done him no harm, has it?"

Thorkell had been too pleased with himself for getting Kolbein's interest to be angry. He patted his wife's shoulder.

"I'm not a King's Landsmen like the Earl and his father, Sigrid. As Kolbein's foster-son, Einar will have more prestige than I can give him and he'll have powerful connections in the Islands. It will be well, you'll see. If I can get Oddi established in Sutherland, and maybe Jon in Caithness, maybe I can find another

nearer home for this one." He laid his hand briefly on her belly and grinned at her. The idea that it might not be another son had clearly not entered his head.

She'd let him dream his dreams but she'd anxiously watched for any sign that this baby would be a girl. She remembered Gudrun laughing that her left breast was larger than her right when she was carrying Marget. Hands cupped inquiringly around her own, she tried to decide whether there was any difference, but she could detect none.

When she went out to the midden, she looked to see if the water she passed was bright yellow or dull, but it looked exactly the same as always. Her feet were no warmer than usual and her hands were never clammy anyway. There was no clue there, and there was still another month to go.

Was her certainty just wishful, as Gudrun thought? Or was it because she did in fact have a maid-child within her?

If she did, what would Thorkell say?

When Gudrun had a second daughter, her man hadn't spoken to her for weeks. It was only when she bore him a son that he had become reconciled to his girls. Would Thorkell feel the same way?

Sigrid suddenly felt guilt that she had done everything possible to ensure this baby was a girl. Taking what God sent was part of life, but she'd actively tried to interfere. Had she done wrong? And would she be made to pay for it?

She sat outside in the evening sunshine, Jon curled asleep in a basket ➔

beside her, stitching new breeks and a tunic for Einar. He came out on soft feet and stood close to her shoulder.

"I don't want to go."

The whisper was so low she wasn't sure if Einar had said the words, or her own heart. She glanced up at her son, who was gazing around the steading as if he would tuck it in his breast and take it with him.

"Kolbein lives in a great keep made of stone. How will I know what to do?"

She drew him close.

"Listen, Einar. Kolbein wouldn't think of taking you into his family if he didn't think you'd make him proud, and your father and I know you will."

"But I'll miss you all," Einar said.

"Even Oddi?" she teased.

the sun reach out across the gently stirring sea. "Anyway, not long now and there'll be another rampaging lad to keep you busy."

She couldn't keep silent any longer.

"Thorkell, I think – I think this bairn may be a girl!" She pulled him round to face her. "I wanted a daughter so much, I did all the things to make a girl, not a boy."

There. She'd said it. Would he beat her? Would he stamp off in a sulk and not speak to her, like Gudrun's man? Would he not love a daughter because she should have been a son?

Thorkell looked thunderstruck. Then a beaming smile spread across his face.

"I hope you're right! A little soft daughter, as beautiful as the day. Just like her mother."

Would he beat her? Would he stamp off in a sulk and not speak, like Gudrun's man?

"Well, perhaps not Oddi," he admitted. "But Bjarni Kolbeinsson will be there, and he's worse!"

"You can deal with Bjarni," she said with a calmness she was far from feeling. "And by the time you come to visit, you'll have another brother." She crossed her fingers, hiding them in her lap. "Or a sister."

He shrugged. That was the future and he couldn't think that far ahead.

That night, Sigrid lay sleepless beside a snoring Thorkell. Should she confess what she'd done, or wait until the child was born? If it was a boy, she needn't say anything. Time enough to tell Thorkell what she'd done if it was a girl.

When Thorkell returned from taking Einar to the tiny island, he was overly hearty. Sigrid knew, despite all the bluster; he missed his son as much as she did.

"No need to worry about our boy," he said, as they sat watching the last rays of

"She'll wind you about her thumb and think you're the most wonderful man in the world. Like her mother." Sigrid was light-headed with thankfulness. "And you'll marry her to a great chieftain."

He put his arm around her, clamping her to his side, and there was understanding in the kiss he dropped on her head.

"It will be a long wait, wife. I shall growl like a bear at any man who comes courting her. Only the best and bravest will be good enough for the daughter of Thorkell Einarsson!" Ⓜ

....

MY MAGIC MOMENT...

The email said, *We're offering you a contract for your novel, Battle For Love.* **I had to get someone else to read it to make sure I wasn't imagining things. Then I did a war-dance!**

Most Amazing Human Achievements

✦ Railways ushered in a new industrial age, forging nations and bringing people together, as well as transporting goods and services, thus improving living standards.

✦ The invention of the printing press was another massive step forward, allowing knowledge to be passed on quickly, efficiently and en masse.

✦ The invention of the computer and internet took the dissemination of knowledge and information among humans to its peak.

✦ Ocean voyages, from galleons in full sail, to steam ships, to massive cruise ships, crossing the oceans was a step into the unknown, but is now a crucial building block for global trade and the spread of knowledge.

✦ One man saved 30,000 bees! Gary Schempp has dedicated his life to finding, rescuing and rehoming bees – and in doing so has contributed in a meaningful way to the very survival of the human race.

✦ The Great Pyramids remain a mystery to this day, but are still an imposing structure in the sands of Egypt, defying science after many centuries.

✦ The Olympics bring people together from all over the world in an atmosphere of "it's not the winning but the taking part" that engenders international friendship and achievement.

The Mona Lisa encapsulates a unique spirit which has entranced people for centuries

✦ United Nations, a global body aiming to secure international friendship and cooperation in the pursuit of world peace.

✦ Democracy, which gives everyone the right to participate in how they are governed.

✦ Wind and solar power make it possible to reduce our dependence on fossil fuels and could end up improving the entire world.

✦ Vaccines were one of the greatest medical advances and led to the decline (and in some cases eradication) of dangerous diseases like TB, polio and smallpox, greatly extending human life expectancy.

All Around The Garden

Can Granny and Shakespeare come to the rescue and resolve a thorny, unforeseen family difficulty?

By Francesca Capaldi

It wasn't looking hopeful. The expressions on the faces of Liz's two grandchildren were glum as they sat side by side on the bench in the play park.

"Well, what do you think?" Anna's voice rose to a merry pitch. She beamed widely, no doubt to encourage a positive reaction.

"I don't think so," said seven-year-old Evie, the younger of the two, not sounding sure. It wasn't a "no", at least.

"I don't want to," Noah followed with.

"Neither do I then." Evie nodded her head decisively.

Anna's shoulders slumped. Liz knew Marc and Anna would be disappointed, now the new baby was on the way.

"I like my last name," said Evie. "Rose, like the flower. Roses are pretty. Can we go back on the slide now?"

"Marc's surname, Lilley, is a flower too," Liz pointed out. "A very pretty one."

"I know, Granny," said Noah. "But I want to keep Rose because it's my name, not because it's pretty." He considered his sister, frowning. "It's *our* name. It belongs to us."

Sometimes Noah seemed so much older than his ten years. He was right, of course – but why he was so keen to keep it after what their father, Stuart, did was a mystery.

Anna and the children had come home one day three years before to find he'd packed and left, with no letter of explanation. He'd also cleared out the bank accounts on his way, leaving them penniless. A lawsuit had only helped recoup some of the money.

"OK, go and play," said Anna. "Those slides won't slide down themselves."

The children jumped down and ran back to the play area. Anna leaned her elbow on the arm of the bench and sighed.

"I so wanted us all to have the same surname. Stuart hasn't even sent cards for the children's birthday since he left – let alone seen them."

Liz patted her arm. "I know, pet. Marc's been much more of a dad to those bairns these last three years than that waste of space ever was. I wish we could come up with a compromise."

"I don't see how." Anna fanned herself with a leaflet she had in her bag. "I'd better phone Marc and let him know."

Marc had taken the children's decision well, considering.

"I can't say I was hopeful, to be honest," he admitted as they sat in the kitchen later that day, watching the kids run round the garden. "Reckon I might have felt the same as Noah at that age."

Anna clutched her large, round belly.

"Well, we can't force them."

"Maybe persuade?" Liz sipped tea. ➤

"You know what kids are like," said Anna. "The more you try to push them, the more they resist."

"Yes – and I should know." Liz raised her eyebrows at Anna, who sighed long and deep. "Marc, have you thought of changing your name from Lily to Rose? That'd be one way to get round it."

"Why should he!" Anna exclaimed.

"It's OK, Anna," said Marc. "I don't object to changing my name in principle. But just the fact it's his name. Sorry."

"No apology needed," said Liz.

Marc had been Stuart's best friend. He'd come to collect him for a game of snooker the day Anna discovered he'd cleared off. Marc hadn't had a clue what his so-called friend had been up to, but had been there to hammer home the point, but her innocent wonder as she touched the edge of the bloom told her not.

"Like I said, a lily is a flower too."

Noah had sidled over, clearly curious.

"What is a lily?" asked Evie.

"There are lots of different ones, but that's one." Liz pointed to a long, white bloom. "That's an arum lily."

"That's pretty, isn't it, Noah?" Evie said as her brother drew nearer.

"Yeah, 'spose."

Evie chatted on, asking Liz the name of the other flowers. Noah stood next to her, nibbling his bottom lip.

In the middle of Liz explaining why she deadheaded flowers, Noah said, "Do you think Dad'll ever come back, Granny?"

"That's it!" yelled Noah. He bolted across the lawn to the kitchen door

help Anna pick up the pieces. Love had blossomed, and they'd married a month after the divorce had come through.

"We'll have to accept the children's decision," said Anna.

"All may not be lost," countered Liz. "I'll get my thinking cap on."

After finishing her tea, Liz joined the children in the garden, where she planned to do a little tidying and replanting for Anna and Marc. They'd enlisted her green fingers when they'd realised their own gardening skills were lacking.

Evie skipped over to her.

"What you doing, Granny?"

"Dead-heading the roses, pet." She picked up her secateurs from the table and began removing the perished blooms.

Evie sniffed the surviving roses. "I like being called after a flower."

Liz wondered if she was trying to

Liz led her grandchildren to the stone bench under the apple tree and sat between them, putting an arm around each.

"Daddy's moved back to Newcastle and has a new wife and is expecting a bairn, like Mummy." So they'd heard via the grapevine. "So I think he'll be a bit busy."

Evie snuggled into Liz.

"Doesn't he love us any more?"

"I'm sure he does – but sometimes it's hard to keep up with an old life when you have a new one."

"We have a new life too," said Noah.

"I guess you do. And me too, come to that," Liz murmured sadly.

Noah's eyes narrowed. "Perhaps we need a new name to go along with it."

"Well, you know what old Mr Shakespeare said."

"Who's he?" said Evie. "A neighbour?"

"You silly billy," said Noah. "He wrote lots of plays. For the theatre."

"That's right, he did." Liz cleared her throat before announcing, "*A rose by any other name would smell as sweet.* That's from one of William Shakespeare's plays. It means it doesn't matter what you're called, you'd still be you, and still as lovely."

She gave them each a hug.

"I guess so." Noah looked unconvinced.

"So, what about Lilley?" Liz suggested.

Noah shook his head. "No. Not Lilley. We need something that's all our own."

At this point they all went, "Hmm," taking on the same expression of deep thought as they gazed at the garden.

After a few moments, Liz pointed to each of the plants, naming them as she went. "Cornflower, peony, geranium, marigold, chrysanthemum…"

"That last one's just silly," giggled Evie.

"But they're all types of flower. Flower. Now that's a surname."

"That's it!" yelled Noah. "Flower!" He jumped on the spot excitedly, before bolting across the lawn and into the kitchen door.

L iz and Evie, arrived at the kitchen as Noah was explaining his idea to his mum and Marc.

"What do you think?" Noah was breathless and expectant.

Anna and Marc looked at each other.

"Well," said Anna, "it would cover us all, roses and lilies both being flowers."

Marc thought for a while.

"Yeah, why not? It seems fair that we should all change our names – not just the children."

"What about you, Evie?" asked Liz.

"I think it's a greeeeat idea."

"Flower it is then," said Anna, beaming. While Marc was chatting to the children, she turned to the older woman. "Liz, are you sure you don't mind the children abandoning the family name?"

"Look Anna, Stuart may be my son, but he's always had a mean streak, just like his father. You've been more of a daughter to me than he was ever a son. He made his choice, and certainly didn't take my feelings into account. You've got my full support."

They joined the others in time to hear Marc pronouncing, "*A rose by any other name would smell as sweet.*"

"Mr Shakespeare said that!" Evie exclaimed.

Marc's eyes widened. "Wow, I'm impressed you know that."

"Granny already told us," Noah said.

Marc rolled his eyes. "Of course. And there was me thinking I was being original."

Liz pointed to Anna's stomach. "Now that's settled, you'd better get the paperwork started. Because it doesn't look like this flower bud will take long to bloom."

"Talking of which," Marc put in, "I'd better go and finish painting the nursery. Nursery? Get it?"

Everyone groaned and Liz gathered them up in a group hug. If her family was happy, she was happy. Ⓜ

....

MY MAGIC MOMENT...

Two years ago I met my cousin Tina, over from Australia, for the very first time. My mother's mum and siblings emigrated there in 1958, so I was overjoyed to meet Tina and catch up.

The Dog And Bone

A quiet weekend minding her aunt's dog? Little did Sarah know…

By Elaine Everest

S arah dear, it's Jo here. Pick up the phone, you know I hate speaking on these awful answer machines."

As much as Sarah loved her Aunt Josephine, she knew that if she stopped work to speak to her it would be another hour at least before she returned to her desk.

"Darling, speak to me. I know you're working at home today, your father told me."

Silently she cursed her father, who had obviously been the recipient of Jo's first telephone call in her search for a mentor cum legal advisor. Her recurring battles with her neighbour were legendary in the family, and were to be avoided at all costs.

Being a freelance illustrator Sarah had the joy of working to her own schedule – but that also meant she was at the beck and call of dear Aunt Jo.

"I promise dear, it's nothing to do with the 'dreaded Dobson man,' but I must speak to you urgently."

Sighing deeply Sarah put down her pen and picked up the phone. She would never get this commission finished until she had calmed her Aunt Jo and sorted out the latest scrape she had got herself into.

"Hi Auntie Josephine, is there something wrong?"

"Of course there's nothing wrong, Sarah. And do stop calling me Auntie Josephine, I've told you before that Jo will do. You make me sound like an aged aunt who wears twinsets and pearls, and crochets toilet roll covers in her spare time."

Considering Aunt Jo was ten years older than her father who had recently retired – he did act his age, by the way – Sarah thought that perhaps she *should* slow down and learn to crochet. The previous time they had met, Aunt ➤

Jo was wearing a shocking pink tracksuit and had been helping out at the local college Student Rag Week where she studied aerobics and anatomy – a strange choice, Sarah had thought at the time.

"Aunt Jo, I have a deadline and I'm terribly behind already."

"I know dear, your father told me you're painting fairies and flowers for that delightful children's book. I thought you had another week to finish them all?"

"Yes I do, but that includes delivery to the publishers." She sighed.

"Well, good – you can finish it down here, then!"

"What? I haven't got time for social visits Aunt Jo. This is my work not a hobby that I can drop whenever I feel like it!"

"I know that dear, and we are all very proud of you, but I need a house-sitter for the weekend. I'm off on an orienteering trip in Wales. My coach leaves at four."

"You haven't given me much notice," Sarah gasped. But she had to admit that the thought of a few days in the depths of the Sussex countryside, where she would be able to finish her work, seemed most attractive.

"Well to be honest, Sarah, the boarding kennels have let me down. It seems that Pogo is on their black list. They've refused to have him back, would you believe?"

In Aunt Jo's eyes, her oversized and over-stuffed dog, Pogo, could do no wrong when in fact he was the terror of the neighbourhood.

If dogs had such things as terrorist groups Pogo would be the leader. He had been known on one occasion to round up all his delinquent canine buddies and launched an assault on the butcher's shop, relieving him of several juicy morsels he was handing to a customer. They were then chased away by the owner – who

was none other than Aunt Jo's neighbour, the dreaded Mr Dobson.

Of course, Aunt Jo assured the family this had nothing to do with her decision to become a vegetarian. But at the same time, she started her vendetta against Mr Dobson who had sworn to have Pogo committed to the dog pound and banned Aunt Jo from his shop.

Three hours later, Sarah pulled into Aunt Jo's street. It hadn't taken her long to pack a few clothes and load her work into the car. A quick phone call to her father had ensured the family knew that she was dog-sitting for Aunt Jo.

She spied a minibus parked outside the house. The driver was trying to herd a group of Jo's friends towards the bus, as well as load the last of the rucksacks into the hold.

"Coo-ee," called a voice from the depths of the bus. Fighting against the flood of eager passengers Aunt Jo staggered onto the pavement.

"Glad I caught you, dear, Pogo's in the lounge waving bye bye to his mummy, his supper's in the fridge, and there's a diet sheet pinned to the door. Oh, and the vicar's wife will be calling round later to collect for the jumble sale. The box is in the shed. See you in a few days."

They both gazed towards the window as Aunt Jo blew kisses to the big hairy face while Sarah stood wondering how she was to remove so many nose marks from the glass and repair the delicate net curtain now hanging at a strange angle around Pogo's neck.

After waving goodbye to the departing bus she carried her few possessions indoors and prepared to meet the dog from hell. Lumbering into the room, Pogo greeted her with much slobbering affection. Fighting off his advances, Sarah managed to wrestle him to the floor.

tapping at the window startled Jo from her concentration.

"Hello my dear, don't let me stop you from your work," she called through the open window. "I know where Jo keeps the jumble, I'll just help myself."

Sarah waved absent-mindedly, her thoughts on the intricate wings of a particularly petite fairy when it crossed her mind that the vicar's wife was bound to encounter Pogo in the garden. Although not aggressive, his over-enthusiastic welcome would be sure to terrify the poor woman.

As quickly as the thought came to her, a terrible scream tortured the air from the direction of the back garden.

Rushing outside, she came across the

"The bones – oh my goodness, look at the bones," she wailed incoherently

"Right, Pogo my boy, it's like this. You and I have got to live with each other for the next few days and I've rather a lot of work to finish. So if I fix you up with an endless supply of bones, will you promise to be a good boy?"

The word *bone* lit a dim bulb in the large, cavernous head. Pogo bounded out of the room to paw at the fridge door.

Good, thought Sarah, *at least we are on the right wavelength; the weekend should be a doddle!*

After an early start the next morning cleaning Jo's slobber-marked window and refitting the curtain, she was able to settle down to her own work. Pogo had retreated to the garden with the first of the meaty bones she'd promised him – it was the size of a man's shin.

The vicar's wife turned up later in the morning to collect the jumble. Her

vicar's wife, hiding her face and sobbing hysterically.

"Mrs Pettigrew what's wrong?" Sarah asked "Has Pogo frightened you?"

The dog was nowhere to be seen, but a large, gaping hole in the hedge indicated his escape into Mr Dobson's garden. The vicar's wife began to mutter incoherently.

"What's that? I'm sorry, Mrs Pettigrew, I can't quite hear you."

"The bones – oh my goodness, the bones," she wailed.

"Oh, the bone. Yes, it is rather large but Pogo is a big dog you know," she answered, wondering why the silly woman was getting so upset about Pogo's snack but also wondering what the dratted dog was doing in Mr Dobson's garden.

She pointed wildly through the hole in the hedge. "Look – the bones, the bones!"

Peering through the hole she spied Pogo sitting proudly in the middle of a ➞

neatly manicured lawn dotted with large, freshly dug holes. His shaggy brown face was now covered in loose earth. He must have spent the last few hours making a minefield of Mr Dobson's lawn in order to find the perfect spot for his bone.

Scrabbling through the hole, Sarah grabbed Pogo by the collar to drag him back to safety. Hopefully she could fill in the holes before Mr Dobson came home.

Dragging Pogo past the vicar's wife Sarah muttered breathlessly, "Nothing to worry about, Mrs Pettigrew – just Aunt Jo's dog being his usual playful self."

But her visitor had started to point and shriek again.

"Look, look at the bones!" Again she covered her eyes, rocking backwards

can deal with," he explained, grim-faced.

"Who can it be? Perhaps it's his ex wife. Aunt Jo said he had been married once a long time ago."

"I don't think we should start to make any assumptions yet." the policeman answered seriously. "Can I ask who discovered the bones?"

Sarah explained about Pogo and how Mr Dobson hated him.

"I think I had better interview the young man," laughed the constable.

Pogo bounded into the room, very pleased to meet a new friend, and the police officer sat on the floor to play with him. It was an instant attraction.

As Sarah helped the young officer pick dog hairs from his uniform, he explained

"This isn't something our local station can deal with. I've called for back-up"

and forwards, moaning to herself.

Sarah shoved Pogo into the house and closed the door on him. Going back to the hedge she again looked through. From the biggest hole protruded a large, whitish bone – not, as she had thought, the meaty fresh one belonging to Pogo, but one that had distinctive bony fingers.

Pogo had dug up a dead person!

She ushered the now hysterical vicar's wife back into the house and left her with Aunt Jo's bottle of best sherry. She then rang the local police to report their find. Hopefully Pogo would not be charged with trespassing.

Very quickly a patrol car arrived. The officer took a few brief notes, then checked Mr Dobson's garden.

Returning to Aunt Jo's house, he accepted the coffee Sarah had just made.

"I've called for back-up – this isn't exactly the kind of thing our local station

that this was his first posting and he was new to the area.

The wailing of sirens announced his colleagues had arrived.

"I'd better go and report to my superiors. I'll let you know what's happening."

"And I should check on the vicar's wife and see about getting her home." She smiled back.

Pogo, exhausted after his interesting day, was snoring softly. The vicar's wife was doing likewise, the bottle of sherry now half consumed.

The following day found next door shrouded in screens to stop prying eyes. Many people came and went with bags and technical equipment.

The vicar, who popped in to see how Sarah was coping, had all the latest news.

"It seems Mr Dobson has been

'assisting the police with their enquiries' but has now gone to stay with his sister in the next village. Have you heard from your aunt yet?"

"I don't have any way of contacting her, but she will be home in the morning – this will all be a bit of a surprise for her!" Sarah answered.

Later that day the police officer popped in to see her.

"We'll have the results of the forensic tests in the morning, Will you be all right on your own? I'm on duty outside all night so if you get frightened just call out."

Snuggling down to sleep that night with Pogo sprawled across the bed, Sarah felt strangely comforted with her two male protectors close at hand.

Sleeping in late the next morning, she opened the curtains to see the team working next door dismantling the screens and packing up to leave. She had just fed Pogo and put the kettle on for coffee when the police officer came in.

"You'll be pleased to know no major crime has been committed next door," he said, fending off Pogo who had greeted his new chum with exuberance.

"The bones came from a skeleton all right – but it seems the skeleton was one stolen from the science lab during Rag Week at the local college. The college name was stamped on the back of the skull. Probably a practical joke – but who would want to bury it in Mr Dobson's garden, God only knows. He's none too pleased, I can tell you."

Aunt Jo arrived back soon after, full of excitement at the news that police were in her neighbour's garden and that strange things were afoot. One of her village friends had excitedly telephoned the group leader and wrongly informed them that Mr Dobson had been arrested.

Jo had hitchhiked home rather than wait another day to travel in the minibus.

"How were things here, my dear? Did Pogo behave himself?"

Sarah explained how Pogo was the local hero discovering the skeleton next door. Aunt Jo started to go a deep shade of red.

"Aunt Jo – you didn't have anything to do with this, did you?" she asked as a sudden thought dawning on her. "You were involved in the Rag Week, weren't you?"

"Darling it was only a prank and that awful man, Dobson, had been so unkind to Pogo. It was so long ago now I had forgotten all about it. Trust Pogo to try to dig the wretched thing up from his garden!" She brightened. "Anyhow, Mr D won't be around much longer. A For Sale board was going up as I came in just now, so can we keep this little prank to ourselves – please? The police have gone, they'll be none the wiser."

I'm not so sure, Sarah thought. *There will be one officer back here this evening at eight to pick me up for a dinner date…* Ⓜ️

MY MAGIC MOMENT...

On May 8, 1995 – as our Queen lit the first beacon to commemorate 50 years since VE Day and fireworks filled the skies – my Old English Sheepdog, Hayley, delivered the first of her litter of nine puppies. Magical!

School Daze

A dreadful school reunion shows Laura that looking forward is the best way to put the past behind you

By Fran Tracey

Thank goodness for that," I told the fresh air that greeted me as I stumbled out of the school hall into the playground.

From stifling and noisy to quiet and chilly. I tugged on my cardie. Cardie? It was my posh cardie, but still... what had possessed me? I might have known my ex-classmates would ignored the "smart casual" dress code in favour of killer heels and slinky frocks.

number of bedrooms she was obliged to find a cleaner for.

Bitter, moi? No, actually, not bitter. Just... well, thrust back to being 17 again. You know that feeling? Where your skin doesn't seem to fit, you're not part of any particular group, and you hesitate before you speak in case your foot speaks for you? Yes, that.

As I had no "plus one" I was squeezed onto the end of a table.

Other people's accomplishments, and those of their close and extended families

I was suddenly thrust back to being 17 again, where I didn't seem to fit in

It had been a last minute decision to attend the 25-year school reunion. I'd been unsure about going, wincing when I passed the cream-coloured invitation stuck on the fridge. I finally decided, out of curiosity, to say yes. I spend a lot of time alone; it might do me good to meet old acquaintances. It could be a laugh.

"Those are, erm... interesting earrings," one ex-classmate had smiled, in between boasting about her career, her children's accomplishments and the

were astonishing. It was like receiving numerous verbal round robins. I kept quiet and drank my warm white wine a little too swiftly.

It was only when they turned to me and asked, "So Laura... husband, kids? News?" that I finally crumpled. Until that point I'd gone under their radar, thought no one had noticed me in the competition for the highest grade achieved at piano by offspring at the youngest age. I have no off-spring, nor a husband. I was regretting coming. I'd thought people might have changed. That had been naïve.

I didn't answer. Instead I simply excused myself.

"I need to make a call," I said, darting towards the doors leading into the playground, hoping they weren't locked.

Deep breaths… that was better.

Well, at least Gillian Johnson hadn't appeared, I thought. That could have made a bad situation worse. I'd looked for her as soon as I entered the room. I'd know her anywhere, even 25 years on.

She'd been one of the reasons I'd accepted so late. Gillian had been our resident school bully. I'd always taken some comfort from the fact that she was an equal opportunities bully – she hadn't only picked on me.

"Hello. You OK?"

A disembodied voice spoke to me, and a puff of cigarette smoke filled the air.

I knew that voice. Gillian Johnson.

I hesitated. I could dart back in, or I could stay. Face the school bully, or face the school boasters?

"Fancy one?"

A slight figure with a mane of red hair appeared from around a corner.

"No thanks." I smiled though, hoping she could see me well enough.

"Nightmare, isn't it?"

I nodded.

"Why did you come?" I asked, curious. We all have our own perceptions of the past. I wondered if Gillian knew what people thought about her back then.

She shrugged.

"Not sure. Thought I might say sorry…"

She trailed off. I was surprised by what she just said.

"Nice earrings." She changed the subject. I swung my head and the dangly bits hit my cheek.

"You like them? I made them. I run my own jewellery business. It's doing OK. More than OK, actually. You?"

"Youth worker. Thought I should put something back, you know."

We both smiled.

Finally I'm glad I've come. I can see that, despite my wobble a few minutes ago, I have truly changed, and it's good to recognise that. I faced my fears by coming here, but I also knew when enough was enough. Clearly Gillian had too. I might still not be part of some groups, but that's OK. I'm content in my cardie, and creating jewellery makes me happy. I have the best job for me.

"Those wonderful earrings… can you make them in purple?" Gillian asked.

"Any colour you like," I smiled, linking arms with her. We bypassed the school hall and, in time honoured Gillian fashion, played truant in the local pub.

There was a past out there to be put to rights. Ⓜ

....

MY MAGIC MOMENT...

After a turbulent time for both kids at school the day they both came home smiling was amazing. You truly are only as happy (or unhappy) as your happiest (or unhappiest) child!

"Don't Be Cruel"

It's a revelation to schoolgirl Yvonne that her gran was one of the original rock 'n' roll teenagers…

By Ginny Swart

Your Mum tells me it's your Prom next month, Yvonne?"

"That's right, Gran. The fifteenth."

Yvonne clicked off her headphones in deference to her grandmother, while Evelyn Hartley settled herself comfortably on the sofa and kicked off her shoes. She grinned at her youngest granddaughter, who had gelled spiky hair and a butterfly tattoo on her shoulder.

"And what are you planning to wear? Something completely outrageous, I

"Yes! We're researched that whole period on the Internet, and the dresses were way cool. Wide elastic belts to make their waist look small, and do you know, they used to wear four or five frilly net petticoats under the skirts?"

"…and dipped them in sugar water to make them stand up," said Evelyn, remembering. "If you wore cotton petticoats you could starch them but you had to use sugar-water for the net ones.

"Granny! Oh, of course, you would remember back then." Yvonne's "in the olden days" remained unspoken.

Yvonne's mother forbade her to accept any rides on her grandad's motorbike

hope? I remember what your cousin Anne wore a few years ago – she was all in black with a glittery lip-ring for the occasion."

Yvonne grimaced. "Black is so out this year. But no worries, Granny, our class had decided we're all going to go retro."

"Retro…?"

"Old fashioned! The sixties look."

"Old fashioned? But it's only…"

Oh dear, yes it is, thought Evelyn. *Sixty years ago. Wow.*

"You mean, dresses with stiff petticoats and full skirts?"

Evelyn Hartley didn't act like an average grandmother. At the weekend she rode on the back of her husband's motorbike, dressed in full black leathers with her thick iron-grey plait tucked up under a scarlet and silver helmet.

The two of them joined breakfast runs out to a pub in the country and sometimes arrived with a throaty roar at Yvonne's house for Sunday lunch afterwards, grinning in delight.

Yvonne's mother Jeanette was tight-lipped with disapproval about her

wayward parents and had forbidden Yvonne to accept rides behind her grandfather – who, she said, drove much too fast for a man his age.

Jeannette made no secret of the fact that she didn't agree with her mother's off-beat view of the world.

Evelyn marched for animal rights, wrote emails to the newspaper about preserving the wetlands and in winter she put food out for the foxes who found their way into town.

All these things gave Evelyn deep satisfaction and she hoped Yvonne would not grow up to be guided by her mother's very conservative view of the world.

"Granny, did you have Proms way back when?"asked Yvonne.

"My goodness yes, that dance was the highlight of our entire school career!" said Evelyn. "We planned it for six months before and talked about it for the rest of the year. Of course, in those days we didn't have much social life."

"So… tell me about yours." Yvonne gave Evelyn her full attention.

"Well, we got together a decorating committee for the school hall…"

"You had to have your dance in the school hall? Poor you – we've booked the ballroom at the Imperial Hotel," interrupted Yvonne. ➡

"Poor *you!*" teased Evelyn. "We had such a lot of fun putting up decorations. Our year decided on an underwater theme, so we painted lots of fish and octopus and starfish and then twisted miles of green and blue crinkled paper streamers across the ceiling. It looked lovely, I can see it now."

"Like a children's party!" giggled her granddaughter.

"We sprayed glitter all over everything and it kept floating down during the evening, so by midnight we were all covered in the stuff. And at the end of the evening the boys all pulled the painted fish off the walls and kept them for souvenirs."

Which reminds me, I haven't danced

I bet you went with someone cool. I mean, for that era."

"We called it 'hip,' and believe me, he was! His nickname was Spike, and he was a bit too hip, according to my mother. She called him a ducktail, just because of his hairstyle, but he was the height of fashion."

"He wore a white tuxedo jacket, with a pink cummerbund, and carried a rat-tail comb in his pink socks."

Evelyn smiled as she remembered how fabulous she'd thought that outfit was – and as for that long, slicked-back hair! Spike had looked the essence of cool, as Yvonne would probably say. The envious, admiring glances he'd received from Evelyn's friends had more than made up for her parents' disapproval.

"Minuets? We Rocked! And we Frugged! We did the Monkey and the Watsui…"

properly for ages, thought Evelyn. *I must do something about that.*

"And what did you do for music? Did you have one of those big bands?"

"No, but the brother of the headmistress brought a whole lot of seven-inch singles and LPs…"

"Collector's items!" breathed Yvonne.

"…And he hooked his record player up to enormous loud speakers on the stage. It was lovely music, real rhythm. We danced to Elvis and Pat Boone and – what was his name, that fellow who sang *Mack The Knife?*"

"No idea," said Yvonne.

"Bobby Darin! That was it. And we danced all night to *Don't Be Cruel* and *Ain't nothin' but a Hound Dog…* and *Blue Suede Shoes…*"

Yvonne shook her head and Evelyn was beginning to feel like a dinosaur.

"Who was your partner, Granny?

"So what was wrong with being a ducktail anyway?"

"Oh, all our parents preferred boys with short back and sides! Or their hair cut flat-top, like Tab Hunter's."

Yvonne looked blank.

"You know – *Young Love?*"

Evelyn started to hum the song but Yvonne shook her head.

"Funny how parents always carry on about hairstyles," she remarked. "Mum can't stand Gavin just because he's shaved his head and he's got a killer tattoo, but he's a really fabulous guy. She just doesn't want to know."

Evelyn had seen Gavin's tattoo, a huge blue spider needled across his shiny, naked scalp, its hairy legs extending over his forehead. Coupled with Gavin's nose-ring and his attitude to the adult world in general, it was no wonder Jeannette hadn't warmed to him.

But Evelyn had often chatted to him about the subject closest to his heart – collecting old movie posters – and she rather liked him. He was a bit inarticulate about other things, but a pleasant enough lad, and he seemed to adore Yvonne.

"Your mum just wants you to be safe and happy," she consoled her granddaughter. "She'd prefer for you to go out with a nice, ordinary chap – maybe with some hair."

Yvonne pulled a face.

"Why not invite Gavin home for lunch, let them get to know each other?"

"Mum doesn't even like me driving around with him, she says his car's an accident waiting to happen – just because he painted a few slogans on it. There's nothing wrong with the engine. He's even got seat belts."

"Perhaps if the slogans weren't so – outspoken," murmured Evelyn. "Those sort of words offend people, you know."

"He's just expressing his freedom of speech. It's his right! Anyway – what did your Spike drive?"

"No one had cars of their own in those days," said Evelyn tartly. "Although Spike worked on Saturdays and bought himself a scooter, but my father wouldn't allow me on it. He drove us to the dance, and he fetched us.

"My dress wouldn't have fitted on the scooter, anyway. As it was, I took up the whole back seat of the Morris."

"Why – did you wear all those net petticoats I was talking about?"

'You've no idea how difficult it was to control them! I had a shocking-pink polished-cotton dress with three extra-

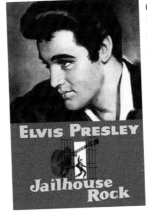

stiff petticoats that I'd spent the whole day starching and ironing, and every time I sat down, the petticoats sort of rose up in a huge cloud. Mind you, I didn't sit down much. We danced every dance."

"What – minuets and stuff?"

"Yvonne! Don't they teach you anything at school?"

Really, the girl had no idea of history, modern or otherwise!

"We Rocked! And we Frugged! We did The Monkey and the Watusi… mind you, that was after we had the Opening Waltz, our headmistress was very traditional. After that we could go wild. And of course, we ended with a slow dance. Real cheek-to cheek stuff. The headmistresses' brother turned the lights down and played *Goodnight Baby*."

"I can't imagine Gavin doing anything called The Monkey," said Yvonne. "He's got great moves, Granny, he shakes his head in double-time to Beyonce better than anyone. But I don't think cheek-to-cheek would be his style somehow."

"You two don't know what you're missing," said Evelyn. "Would you like to see my matric dance pictures?"

"You bet!"

Evelyn rummaged around in a drawer. "Here we are. All my old school photos."

Yvonne looked at the small black and white prints held in with photo corners, but couldn't recognise her grandmother in any of them.

"This is practically an antique, Gran." She turned the page to a big group picture entitled *Prom, 1964*.

"Which one are you, Granny?" ➤

"Here I am. I was always the tallest so they put me at the back for photos. Luckily Spike was tall too."

A gangly girl with short blonde hair and odd comma-shaped curls stared out in the glare of the flashlight, next to a boy with a bad case of acne and a huge quiff of oily hair combed back from his forehead.

"That was Spike?" Yvonne couldn't hide her disappointment. "And that's you? I would never have recognised you! You look just like everyone else!"

"Probably because I was trying to look like Sandra Dee. She was everyone's ideal but when I was seventeen and nearly six feet tall. I hadn't worked out that everyone has their own style and short, blonde and curly just wasn't mine."

"I can't imagine you ever wanting to be short, blonde and curly, Granny. You always look so elegant."

"Thank you, sweetie. I call it the tailored look."

It had taken Evelyn several years to discover she looked good in well-cut suits and dresses without any fashionable jangly bits and pieces. Just after her twenty-first birthday she'd thrown out all her full skirts and fussy petticoats and concentrated on perfecting a style of dressing which had served her well for the past fifty years. With a few nods

to changing fashions, of course.

"But that looks like a really smooth dress, Gran. Exactly what we're all going to wear… boat neck, little cap sleeves and loads of petticoats. Pity you didn't keep it."

Evelyn couldn't imagine Yvonne in anything cute and frilly. Her tall and slender granddaughter hadn't realised it yet, but she was destined for stylish simplicity, just like her Gran.

And Gavin was probably going to turn out like Spike in the end, too. A good family man with, hopefully, a streak of devilment in him. Although he'd probably start growing some hair, instead of the other way round.

"Oh, there's your grandad home," she said, getting up to greet the tall, stooped man with a hug. "Yvonne and I have just been looking at our old Prom photos, darling. She didn't even recognise us!"

"You mean… Granddad was Spike?" Yvonne looked stunned.

"Of course! I wasn't going to let a lovely lad like this one get away!" smiled her grandmother, patting his bald pate. "When he lost the ducktail, he lost his nickname."

"But he gained a wife," said her grandfather, kissing Evelyn. "Your Prom, hey? We haven't been dancing for quite a while. Think you can still rock 'n roll, sweetheart?"

"Fancy even asking!" said Evelyn, taking his hand and giving a twirl. "The question is, can you still do the Mashed Potato?" Ⓜ

MY MAGIC MOMENT…

I can't think of any single moment more magic than all the others, but the biggest rush of excitement I ever felt was when my husband announced we'd been transferred to Hong Kong. Five magic years!

Celebration Time

Muffin Burgers

Ingredients (Makes 16)

- 350g plain flour
- 15g baking powder
- 185g caster sugar
- 2 medium eggs, beaten
- 185g melted butter
- 240ml whole milk
- 1tsp vanilla extract
- 10g sesame seeds
- 600g chocolate frosting
- 250g golden marzipan
- Red and green piping icing to decorate

1. Preheat the oven to 190°C, Fan Oven 170°C, Gas Mark 5. Grease and flour 16 x muffin tins. Put the flour, baking powder and sugar in a bowl, and make a well in the centre.

2. Add the egg, butter, milk and vanilla and mix to a thick batter. Divide equally between the tins, smooth tops, sprinkle with seeds and bake for 25min until risen and golden. Cool for 10min then turn on to a wire rack.

3. Slice the muffins in half. Put the chocolate frosting in a piping bag fitted with a 1cm diameter plain nozzle and pipe a coil of icing over the bottom half of each muffin.

4. Roll out marzipan thinly. Cut into 6cm squares to resemble cheese slices, and lay on top of the chocolate icing. Pipe with red icing to resemble ketchup. Top with the other muffin halves. Pipe with green icing to resemble lettuce. Store in an airtight container until ready to display. → P 89

RECIPE AND FOOD STYLING: KATHRYN HAWKINS PHOTOGRAPHY: STUART MACGREGOR

Seller Beware!

Not another pesky cold-calling bogus tradesman – Megan had to get over to Gran's, and pronto…

By David Wass

Megan pleaded into the phone while she manoeuvred little Ella into her bright green hoodie.

"Please, Gran, tell him to leave. There's nothing wrong with the roof."

The quicker she got from her flat to Gran's lovely old house the better, otherwise things could get out of hand.

"I don't care what the nice man says. If you are worried about the tiles, I know someone who'll check them out for you at the weekend…"

The so-called builder she'd let in shouldn't even have got as far as the front door. He couldn't have missed the signs saying *No Cold Calling.*

Actually, he wasn't the only halfwit who'd ignored the notices. A young salesman from a double-glazing business had called on Gran three months ago while Megan was on a family holiday. He'd refused to leave until a contract had been signed.

"Yes, Gran – but appearances can be deceptive," Megan said, almost dropping the phone as she zipped up her three-year-old's coat.

As soon as she'd heard about the contract, Megan had told the company that the rep had ignored the signs. After a lot of hassle, they'd eventually torn it up, but the old lady was so livid that Megan had feared for her health.

"That sort should be locked away, going around wasting people's time," she'd fumed, her walking stick thumping

the carpet. "How would they like it if it happened to them?"

After that, Megan had put up more signs. To no avail, since a few weeks ago a slick, older man had been determined to tell Gran about a wonderful new gas company that would save her a fortune.

He'd been there for hours, and there had been nothing but trouble after that visit, too. Fortunately, the magistrate had seen things her way.

"OK, then, Gran, make him some tea if you want to," Megan gasped, shrugging into her own waterproof jacket. "But whatever you do, don't… Gran?"

Dial tone. Megan dumped the phone on its cradle, gathered up Ella, and dashed out of the flat to her car.

"Yes, darling, I know you like seeing Great-Gran," she said brightly, as she buckled Ella into her seat.

Forty minutes later, Megan skidded to a stop behind a dirty white van opposite the gate with one of the *No Cold Calling* notices attached to it.

"Let's go, Ella," she said, glancing round. Her little girl's bunny rabbit bonnet rested against the wing of the car seat, her eyes were closed, and her chest was gently rising and falling.

"Ah well, won't be long," Megan murmured, and seconds later she was careering up the path to the front door.

"Is that you, dear?" Gran's voice wavered from the kitchen.

Megan rushed in to find her relative standing by the sink. Alone.

"Where is he?" Megan gasped, her head swinging frantically left and right.

"Hello, there, love. Kettle's on. Tea in two minutes."

"Yes, right."

She flew into the sitting-room. No one. Upstairs, the bathroom was deserted. As were the bedrooms. She took the stairs back down two at a time.

"Tell me where he is, Gran. Please."

"Shall I pour straight away, dear?"

"No." Megan rocketed out of the back door, across the lawn, and peered through the window into the shed. Nothing.

Spinning round, she raced off to the rear of the building – and stopped dead.

"Oh, no!" Megan groaned at the sound of hammering on the underside of a heavy wooden hatch built into a concrete plinth.

Hurriedly, she yanked back the bolt and lifted the lid of what used to be a coal cellar. A stocky figure emerged, his smart grey suit covered in grime.

"All I said was I'd do a little job for her," he muttered, shielding his eyes from the cold light of the drizzle-damp day.

"Best go that way," Megan said. She pointed to the side of the house.

He shot off. The lid fell back with a thud.

By the time Megan reached her car, the conman's van was already out of sight.

Ella was stirring. Megan smiled as she unfastened her seatbelt.

All things considered, the so-called roofer had been pretty lucky. He couldn't have had more than twenty minutes confinement, whereas the unfortunate boiler rep had been stuck in the shed for nearly three hours.

OK, maybe locking people up was a bit extreme – but if "that sort" chose to ignore the No Cold Calling signs, they should expect to have their time wasted.

Just like Gran had done with that double-glazing salesman. Ⓜ

MY MAGIC MOMENT...

The day I arrived at my grandson's first birthday party, held out my arms for a cuddle, and he toddled from his mummy to me. They were his very first steps!

Most Iconic Movie Moments

FANCY THAT!

✦ **The door scene from** *Titanic*... The debate lives on about whether the two of them could both have fitted on the door...

✦ **The opening scene of** *The Sound of Music*... What could be more uplifting than Maria's joyful song among the hills?

✦ **"There's no place like home" from** *The Wizard of Oz*... How to choose the most memorable moment in this classic movie? But the clicking of those ruby slippers has to be just the best!

✦ **The Tiffany's scene from** *Breakfast at Tiffany's*... Holly's arrival outside the famous New York jewellery store doesn't need dialogue to be memorable. Who other than Audrey Hepburn could make a pastry and a cup of coffee look so glamorous?

✦ **"I'll have what she's having" from** *When Harry Met Sally*... Apparently, this scene is responsible for throngs of tourists flocking to Katz's Delicatessen in New York City.

✦ **"You are a toy!" fight scene from** *Toy Story*... While stranded at the gas station, Woody and Buzz Lightyear quarrel as Woody tries to get Buzz to accept that he is, in fact, a toy.

✦ **The shower scene from** *Psycho*... Shot in black and white, with chocolate syrup for blood, it still freaked us all out!

✦ **The spaghetti scene from** *Lady And The Tramp*... Plenty of humans have tried to recreate this, but the dogs are far cutesier!

The phone home scene from ET... Sweet, pure, child like, innocent and uplifting... just like the movie

Brain Boosters

Missing Link

The answer to each clue is a word which has a link with each of the three words listed.
This word may come at the end (eg **HEAD** linked with **BEACH, BIG, HAMMER**), at the beginning (eg **BLACK** linked with **BEAUTY, BOARD** and **JACK**) or a mixture of the two (eg **STONE** linked with **HAIL, LIME** and **WALL**).

ACROSS

1 Back, Petty, Point (4)
3 Butter, Milk, Shy (7)
8 Clock, False, Fire (5)
9 Blithering, Box, Useful (5)
10 Book, Cabin, Jam (3)
12 Bright, Off, Plug (5)
14 Cake, Coin, Sign (5)
16 Cheese, Last, Poll (5)
20 Clamp, Spin, Wagon (5)
22 Arctic, Cub, Trot (3)
24 Extra, Print, Scale (5)
25 Gothic, Idea, Paperback (5)
27 Box, Eye, Hostile (7)
28 Business, Streak, Well (4)

DOWN

1 Light, Roman, Wick (6)
2 Dead, Red, Salt (3)
3 Close, Jacket, Trousers (6)
4 Ball, Pitch, Team (7)
5 Biting, Scissors, Thumb (4)
6 Artist, Military, Parlour (6)
7 Clef, Double, Drum (4)
11 Health, News, Turn (4)
13 Baked, Crown, Time (4)
15 Get, Lead, Man (7)
17 Book, Fight, Slip (6)
18 Court, Elbow, Lawn (6)
19 Liquid, Mask, Tent (6)
21 Action, Going, Wire (4)
23 Board, Saw, Work (4)
26 Detector, Down, White (3)

Turn To Page 155 For Solutions

Hidden word in the shaded squares: _____

Make A Wish

Sometimes wishes really do come true, especially with a little help from friendly neighbourhood fairies…

By Elizabeth McKay

Gail looked at the chaos stretching in front of her and sighed. Where to begin? Steve had been the gardener, the DIYer and the decorator. She'd taken care of the house and cooked the meals. Not very PC in today's world of all being equal, but it had worked for them, and they were happy. Or so she'd thought.

Now Steve was living with his company's new Head of Public Relations. A stunner by all accounts. They could probably afford to pay someone to do the chores, while Gail struggled to get to grips with the central heating system in the new little semi-detached she'd moved into two weeks ago. And all the time reminding herself there was no point being bitter. The only person hurting was herself.

This morning, when she woke up, the sun was shining. She couldn't put it off any longer. It was time to tackle the garden. It wasn't just the enormity of the task that troubled her. It was the fear that she might come into contact with her neighbour. That she'd be forced into polite conversation, and somewhere along the way she'd have to explain about Steve, and the cliché she'd become as the wife rejected for a younger, more glamorous model.

She'd met her neighbour Karen the day she'd moved in. Gail had been making her way up the path carrying a load of boxes, and Karen had been coming out of her own front door, accompanied by her little girl.

They'd stood for a moment and chatted. Enough time to introduce themselves and for Karen to welcome Gail to the cul-de-sac, and to say if there was anything she needed she only had to ask.

A magic wand might be a good thing, Gail thought now, as she stared at the micro-jungle in front of her. She decided to start by tackling the area that ran along the fence separating the two gardens. Even to her unskilled eyes she could tell the shrubs were unruly and overgrown. It was time to give the new secateurs she'd bought yesterday their inaugural outing.

Half an hour in and Gail suddenly realised she was humming. Forty minutes and she was smiling, and thinking how lovely the border would look in the spring, carpeted with crocuses. Another fifteen minutes passed before she heard the voice. She looked behind her, thinking someone must have come round from the front. But there was no one there.

The voice spoke again. This time she looked up and saw a small porcelain-like face peeping over the top of the fence.

"Hello," said the little girl, "I'm Emily. What's your name?"

"I'm Mrs…" she stopped herself, not quite sure who she was now. "I'm Gail," she said.

➜

"It's nice to meet you, Gail," said Emily. "I'm four-and-a-half."

"You're very tall for four-and-a-half," said Gail, "if you can see over the fence."

The little girl giggled. "I'm standing on a garden chair."

"Ah," Gail nodded.

Would you like me to help you dig your garden?" asked Emily. "We're learning how to help people at nursery."

"That's very kind of you," said Gail. "But I don't think you should go anywhere without checking with your mum."

"I'll go and ask her," said Emily. And then she disappeared.

Gail had started clearing up the debris Wilsons at number seven bought a new car last week, and the twins who lived across the road were on holiday. They were Emily's very best friends and she missed them lots.

Gail was busy tidying up what she thought might have the potential to be a small vegetable plot when she heard Emily calling her name.

"Gail, quick! Come and see this."

Gail went to investigate and found the little girl standing in front of a rowan tree in the bottom corner of the garden.

"Look, Gail," said Emily, pointing to a white mass at the base of the trunk. Emily's eyes were shining with excitement.

The little girl plucked a dandelion and blew gently so the seeds floated away

left over from the shrub massacre when she heard a voice again. This time it was Karen peering over the fence.

"Hi, Gail, I'm so sorry I haven't invited you in for coffee yet. We're doing up the kitchen and everything's a bit of a muddle."

"I know the feeling," said Gail.

"Emily says you've asked her to help in the garden."

"Well… I didn't actually… I mean…"

A small head popped up above the fence and smiled.

"If she'd like to," Gail submitted.

"Only if you're sure she won't be a bother," said Karen. "And only for an hour at the very most. I don't want her taking up all your time."

Emily chatted the whole time, going from one subject to another without stopping to draw breath. Gail learned a lot about her new neighbours. Mrs Brown's dog had just had five pups, and apparently Mrs Brown wasn't at all happy about it, blaming the milkman's border terrier. The

"Fairies," she said. "You've got fairies at the bottom of your garden."

Gail bit her lip in an effort not to laugh. "They're not fairies, sweetheart, they're weeds. Dandelions that have gone to seed. I'll have to dig them all out later."

"Oh no, Gail!" Emily protested. "They're fairies. Look how small and pretty they are."

She plucked one of the stems and shook it gently until several of the seeds came away and started floating through the air. Emily reached out for one and held it gently in her hand.

"Now, it's your turn to catch one, Gail. Quick, before they all fly away."

Gail stretched out and caught one of the seeds in her hand.

"Now we have to make a wish and let them go," said Emily.

Gail watched the little girl's face screw up in earnest concentration. Then she opened her hands and released the fairy.

"I wished the twins would come back from their holidays soon," said Emily.

"What did you wish for, Gail?"

"Oh, just boring, grown up things," said Gail, letting go of her own fairy. "Now how about some orange juice and a biscuit as a reward for all our hard work?"

Gail went inside to attend to the drinks and when she came back out the clump of dandelions had gone.

"I blew them all away," said Emily. "Now they're going to make other people's wishes come true."

Gail thought it more likely they'd give the other people aggravation as they battled to keep the weeds under control, but she didn't say that to Emily.

That night Gail slept better than she had for months. She was delighted to see the sun shining again when she woke and could hardly believe how much she was looking forward to working in the garden.

She'd been out for an hour when Emily's face appeared at the fence.

"Hello, Gail. Guess what? The fairy made my wish come true."

"Really?"

"The twins are coming home from their holidays today."

"That's wonderful, Emily. I know how much you've been missing them."

"But I can still help you in the garden. They won't be back until after tea."

"That's very kind of you."

"Only if you're sure she's not being a nuisance," said Karen, appearing at her daughter's side.

"Not at all," Gail smiled, "I enjoy her company."

"In that case," said Karen, "I'll make some sandwiches for lunch. It's the least I can do after you two have been working so hard. I'll bring them over once I've hung out the washing."

A couple of hours later the two women were seated on Gail's patio while Emily did more exploring in the garden.

Gail found herself telling Karen about her reasons for coming to live here. She surprised herself by not crying, and even more so when she realised how much of the bitterness seemed to have evaporated, leaving only tinges of sadness and regret.

Their conversation was interrupted when Emily appeared, clutching another dandelion.

"I think these fairies must have stayed behind to give us another wish," said Emily. Then she blew gently and watched the seeds soar away in the breeze.

"I wished the twins would bring me a stick of rock from their holidays," she said. "What did you wish for, Mummy?"

"I wished my washing would be dry enough for me to iron when I go back," Karen sighed.

"What about you, Gail?" asked Emily.

"I didn't make a wish," said Gail. "I said thank you instead." She looked at the faces of her new friends and smiled. "Thank you to the fairies who've already made my wishes come true." **MW**

MY MAGIC MOMENT...

Surrounded by family and friends at the launch of my first picture book about a wee granny and a magic bag. It was a magical moment in every sense.

The Egg Hunt

Their rivalry was as intense as their friendship. Izz must not be allowed to find that huge stash of chocolate…

By Camilla Kelly

Her main competition, Retta decided as she glanced along the starting line, would be Izz. Look at her, already edging a toe ahead. Just because she'd spent a bit of time at the gym, she thought she was Usain Bolt.

Izz met Retta's eye and winked. Retta put on her best "bring it on" face but it just made them both giggle.

Izz was her best friend. But no one was going to get between Retta and the chocolate eggs hidden in the church garden for the Easter hunt. The kids had already had their turn, now it was the adults'. Rumour was, one of the eggs – the first prize – weighed a kilo.

It seemed like forever since Retta had had any chocolate, which was sad, because it was one of her favourite things. But she and Izz had decided to join a weight loss club for Lent, something they'd both put off for years.

For six weeks they'd been so disciplined they bored everyone to tears. They'd stuck to menu plans, measured everything precisely, purged their houses of sugary and fatty snacks – a move that had not been popular with Retta's young children or Izz's sweet-toothed boyfriend. They'd practised a buddy system and constantly talked each other out of reaching for a doughnut at the café or chips at the takeaway.

The Easter target kept them going. At each weekly weigh-in, they would celebrate their success by talking eagerly about the first treat they'd have once the diet was over.

Retta had actually had *dreams* about this chocolate-filled garden.

The whistle blew and the crowd broke across the lawn like a pack of startled geese, turning in every direction, the women getting their heels stuck in the grass. Half of them were too busy laughing to be any use.

Retta, wearing trainers, rushed off with purpose. She had a strategy. Flora Williams, though kind enough to organise this charity event every year, was unimaginative, so Retta went for the places she remembered Flora using.

First, she looked in the veg patch,

and found a crème egg. Very nice – but much too small for her ambitions.

She glimpsed Izz digging about behind a rose bush and getting chased off by an angry bee. Chuckling, Retta headed to the pond. She took a short cut between the greenhouse and the fence, noting with pleasure that unlike last year, she could squeeze through without trouble.

She found another tiny egg in the leaf-skimmer. Around her, all the chocolates were being found and snatched up with delight. She was running out of time.

Hurrying, she checked the ceramic duck perched on the edge of the pond. Last year the children's first prize had been hidden here.

Impatiently, Retta scooped up the duck. Yes – joy! – there was something inside its hollow body. She reached in and triumphantly drew out… another tiddler.

At the same time there was a shout from across the lawn. Someone had found the prize. Retta craned to see – was it Izz?

She dropped the small egg and hurried towards the commotion. People were breaking into applause.

The first prize was indeed something to behold. Wrapped in gold paper, it seemed it was so heavy the winner, Hayley Mason, struggled to lift it over her head in triumph. So it wasn't Izz who'd found it.

Izz caught Retta's eye and shrugged.

"Never mind," Izz said. "There's always next year."

"And Hayley looks like she could afford some fattening up."

Izz snorted a giggle. "Unlike us."

"I wouldn't have eaten it anyway," Retta said. Izz raised an eyebrow. "Really. I'm halfway to my goal weight, I'm not going to stop now."

"But all that stuff about dying for chocolate…"

"That was before I managed to get into my vintage jeans again."

"So why did you try so hard to find the giant egg?" Izz said, perplexed.

"To take temptation out of your path. I take my job as your weight-loss partner very seriously, I wanted to be sure you didn't fall off the wagon. You're looking so great."

"Oh," Izz said, laughing. "I was doing exactly the same thing!"

Retta slipped her newly slender arm through Izz's, pleased.

"I guess we're going to be partners for a while longer, then."

Hayley had cracked the egg and was offering the chocolate around. Retta looked at Izz. Izz looked at Retta. Together, their arms still linked, they walked away from temptation. Ⓜ

....

MY MAGIC MOMENT…

The first time my friend took me horse-riding, it was a temperamental spring day, and as we came over the hill I remember how beautiful the sunlight breaking over the moorland was.

Where's The Easter Bunny?

Not everyone follows the same traditions. But it's not so easy explaining that to a four-year-old...

By Glynis Scrivens

"Mummy, why didn't the Easter bunny come to our house?" Four-year-old Emma's bottom lip was wobbling. "He went to Audrey's house."

Audrey was her friend at nursery.

How could Sue answer this question? She'd felt bad fibbing at Christmas time about Santa Claus. But at least that had been part of her own upbringing. She wondered now why her parents had never gone along with the Easter bunny story. She'd find an opportunity to ask her mother. Meanwhile what could she say?

Emma didn't wait for her to answer. She was too busy stuffing a small toy rabbit into an old pink bed sock. As Sue watched, Emma carefully put the sock toy onto the back-door mat and put a carrot beside it. Then she surveyed her handiwork with great satisfaction.

"What are you doing there?" Sue couldn't help asking.

"I thought if the Easter bunny has a friend to play with here, he might come," she said. "And he might stay. They could eat the carrot."

It was bedtime. Sue tucked her young daughter into bed and for the umpteenth time told her a story she'd invented about Peter Rabbit. She often borrowed characters and settings from Emma's favourite books as the springboard for her bedtime stories.

Emma's eyes slowly closed, reopened, and then, rolling over, she was asleep. Sue continued with her story for a few minutes, just to be on the safe side, before tiptoeing outside to put the kettle on.

Thing was, she could

remember feeling the same as Emma when she was young. The boy next door to her always woke on Easter Sunday to find lots of eggs left by the Easter bunny.

One year Sue pretended to fall asleep. After her mother had finished tucking her in and walking outside, she'd carefully opened her bedroom window and left it ajar. Just enough for a good-sized rabbit to squeeze through.

Usually she was too scared to have her window open at night. Her older brother had told her there were monsters living in their garden. But just this once she'd be brave. If her window was open, maybe the Easter bunny would notice that when he was next door delivering Gary's eggs?

She knew Santa came down chimneys but nobody ever said how the Easter bunny got inside houses. Why not through a window? So maybe he'd simply been locked out?

It didn't bring her the desired visit by the bunny, and she still remembered the disappointment that morning.

Next morning Sue woke to find Emma tugging at her arm. "Can you please open the back door? I want to see if the Easter bunny came."

Slowly Sue pulled on her dressing gown. She knew there were no chocolate eggs on their back landing.

There was a scream of delight when she opened the door.

"Look!" shrieked Emma. "He came. He ate the carrot."

Sue had eaten it, leaving teeth marks and not quite finishing it. Not her ideal supper, but now she felt glad she'd thought of it.

The little rabbit toy was out of the sock. Emma was entranced.

"They played," she said happily.

And that seemed to satisfy her.

Easter Sunday was a busy day. Sue had invited her parents over for a roast lunch and her in-laws came to afternoon tea. All were bearing chocolate eggs and bunnies and even a few carrots. Emma had enough chocolate to last her for weeks.

When everyone had gone home, and she was tucking her daughter into bed with another Peter Rabbit story, Emma interrupted her.

"Do you think the Easter Bunny will come next year, Mummy?" she asked.

Sue noticed she didn't ask about eggs.

"He might want to play with your rabbit toy again," she said.

"Yes, and we could give him a carrot too." Then came the question Sue had been waiting for all day.

"Will he bring me Easter eggs?"

Sue reminded her of the ones she'd received from her grandparents.

"Maybe he thought you didn't need them," she said. "Maybe he takes them to children who won't be getting any?"

Emma smiled. "That's a good idea."

Sue thought so too. MW

MY MAGIC MOMENT...

The day I got the keys to our very own beach house in Coolum, a place I've come my whole life to find peace. And knowing my adult children can now escape to its tranquility too.

Hunting For Treasure

How will Lucy ever manage to reconcile her materialistic mum and her salvage-obsessed boyfriend?

By Jo Styles

"That Dan of yours is such a cheapskate," Lucy's mother muttered outside Home And Heart Furniture on Saturday morning.

She leaned closer to the window, salivating over the ultra-modern dining room scene. All glass and chrome, it wouldn't look out of place on a spaceship.

"If you need a new table and chairs you should buy some, not do some up," she went on. "You had such lovely things when you were married to Ryan."

She gave the bulging carriers Lucy held a look of pure disgust. They'd just been scrounging old emulsion paint from Lucy's friends.

"It's not as if Dan even lives with you. I mean, he can't tell you what to do."

"Mum, I'm not buying anything new," Lucy said patiently. "We have a plan and we made it together."

"That plan belongs in a skip, the same as those old chairs he found." Her mum bustled onwards. She liked to make it clear she thought of Dan as a pile of discarded junk himself. "I'm nipping in here." She headed towards a shop. "I'm going to get the kids some treats. They'll need some after today."

"Mum, they are not being tortured."

"If you say so…"

After splitting up from her ex, Lucy had rented a mid-street terrace just outside of town. After the long walk to reach it, as soon as she pushed the door open, a keening whine reached her.

"We're back with the paint," she called.

The noise came from The Workshop, as her kids now called the dining room. Her mum's nose wrinkled as she walked into a haze of smelly dust.

Lucy's children, Chloe and Poppy, aged ten and eight, worked on a chair each, sandpaper blocks in hand. Dan himself leaned over an ancient table, his noisy sander working overtime as his thirteen-year-old-son, Jordy, supervised. They all wore face-masks and goggles, looking like a cross between scientists and bank robbers.

"It would have been far easier to have bought something new –"

The sander might have drowned out Lucy's mother's latest whinge had Dan not chosen that moment to switch it off.

"What colours did you get?" he asked, ignoring her remark. He hurried over and peered into Lucy's carriers like an eager schoolboy. "That all looks great."

Always a peacemaker, he smiled over at her mum. "Janice, I've got something for you." From the corner he picked up her surprise and lofted it over. "Your very own chair. You can have one like ➤

The chairs
would look
great with
a coat of
paint

everybody else. It will need a good sanding before you paint it, of course."

Janice's lips pursed.

"Hauled it from another skip, did you?"

"I did actually. Jordy said there was one close to his school, so I popped over. The man throwing it out said he didn't mind. Anyway, I thought you'd like to join in?"

He gave her a look that suggested he felt sure she wouldn't.

That meant she just had to.

"Fine, but I'm working in the kitchen. It's far too crowded in here. You could work with me, Lucy. I wanted another chat anyway."

Oh wonderful, Lucy thought. *There's another Q&A session coming up.*

that is where your Ryan should end up, after meeting that floozy in a hotel –"

Mercifully before she could go on, Dan swept in with his sander, yanking its cord after himself like a tail.

"Right ladies, are you ready to get your bottoms sanded?"

"I assume you mean seats," Janice corrected, refusing to even smile.

"Exactly. I need to get you two finished. Everybody else is just about ready for the great paint debate."

"The what?" Janice curled her lip.

"We have to divvy up the colours for the chairs. If we weren't doing this on a shoestring I'd use primer and undercoat first but beggars can't be… too fussy."

All this cost-cutting was encouraging the girls to be very creative, she realised

The extra chair might not be identical but it was the same basic design – a hard wooden seat and a back with spindles. Janice toiled over it, out in the kitchen. She'd refused to wear a face mask and goggles. Still, at least she couldn't snipe over Dan's safety measures.

"Lucy…" She lowered her voice as her sandpaper scraped along the chair's leg. "You've never said precisely why Dan and his wife split up. I would like to know, since it looks like he might well move in with you and my grandchildren."

"I did tell you, Mum. It was because of irreconcilable differences."

"That could mean anything. Did his penny-pinching drive the woman insane?"

"Don't be silly." Lucy applied more pressure to her own sanding-block. "There's nothing wrong with Dan. I'm getting divorced, too. It doesn't mean I deserve to be on the scrapheap, does it?

"Huh," said her mum. "Maybe not, but

"What a lovely turn of phrase. I have some treats for the kids. I'll hand those out now." Janice stomped off into the dining room as if all set to stage some kind of strike amongst the workforce using chocolate as an incentive.

Dan, dust mask sitting on his head like a party hat, couldn't find a smile.

"She really hates me, doesn't she?"

"No, don't be silly," Lucy soothed. "She always takes a while to warm to people. You just be yourself."

"Speaking of which, have you told her yet? You did say you planned to as she was coming round?"

"Er… no, not yet. Soon. Why don't I get the Hoover out and start cleaning up some of the dust before we paint?"

When at last everything that needed sanding had been finished and a clean-up had taken place, Dan gathered them all in the dining room.

"Right," he said as he arranged all the paint they'd managed to find in a line across the carpet. "We have light blue, charcoal, sage green, a very mellow lilac, baby pink, red, cream, white and… gold."

"Gold?" Janice echoed. "I didn't know you had gold."

Without a word Dan picked up the can. With a little bow he handed it over. "I'm sure this will suit you, Janice."

She didn't argue. "Fine," she said. "So long as nobody wants to fight me for it?"

Nobody took up her invitation.

"Can I have the red, please?" Poppy cried instead.

"Can I have the blue?" Jordy asked.

"Can I have the pink?" asked Chloe. Remarkably, the handing out of the colours didn't end up in tears or a bad case of the sulks.

"I'll paint the underside of the table with the white," Dan told them all. "I'll leave the top untouched and just varnish it. It'll all look lovely. You'll have a multi-coloured dining room, Luce, everyone with a chair they've worked on themselves."

Lucy grinned. When he put it like that, it did sound rather special. He handed out brushes next; those he'd also scrounged.

"There you go," he said to Janice.

"I've never painted anything before in my life," she replied.

"Well, there's a first time for everything."

Back in the kitchen, on more newspaper he'd cadged, she set to brushing on a layer of rich, shiny gold.

Lucy, meanwhile, painted her own chair. She could hear the girls yammering on to Dan in the dining room about school and homework and what they'd like to do to their bedrooms colour-wise if their landlord agreed. All this cost-cutting was encouraging them to be very creative.

"You still haven't told me." Her mum's dour tones interrupted her eavesdropping. "Why did Dan get divorced?" She waved her golden brush. "Is there something you're trying to hide from me?"

"No." Lucy twitched where she stood.

"Then tell me."

All the blood left Lucy's stomach.

"OK. I will," she said regardless. "Dan deserves to be seen in a different light. If you can manage that, Mum?"

Still the subject left her pulse racing.

Ten minutes later, she charged into The Workshop.

"Dan, Mum's had a change of heart. How do we get the gold off her chair? Luckily, she's only painted half a leg."

He frowned as the kids worked on.

"It's probably best just to let it dry, then paint over it later."

"OK. Good idea. What colours do we have left for her?"

"There's that nice soft lilac, if she'd like that? Why did she change her mind? Did you tell her about what you did… at last?"

"Er… no. I told her about your ex instead while I was working up to it. She decided gold wasn't suitable then. It'd looked like she was rubbing things in."

"I didn't think she'd ever worry about me, to be honest."

"Me neither. This must be… progress." Lucy carried off the can.

In the kitchen Janice waited with a clean brush and a pained expression.

"Go on – tell me more," she said in a low voice. ➜

"Well." Lucy took a deep breath. "After Dan's wife booked that surprise holiday I just told you about, and ordered a new bespoke kitchen she went out and ordered a new car on a payment plan and then she bought loads of new clothes. They ended up in even more debt."

"No wonder he likes to keep costs down," said her mum. "You really should have told me all this ages ago.

"Still, I do think you're going a tiny bit too far trying to please him. Look at you, fixing up old furniture with paint you've practically begged for."

"Yes, look at me."

"Tell me more about his ex." Janice frowned. "I want to hear it all. The woman sounds like a nightmare."

D an bounded in half an hour later. "We're about done. How about you two? Let's move your chairs in and see what everything looks like together."

Being careful of the still tacky paint, he managed to get their chairs into the dining room. He settled them down on still more pages of newspaper around the table. "There, what do you think, everybody?"

"It looks great," said Lucy.

Everybody agreed. Even her mum said, "Bravo," rather loudly. Clearly she was relieved Dan hadn't turned out to be the same kind of skip-fodder as Lucy's ex.

Peering at her colourful chairs and lovely new table, Lucy took Dan's hand and held it tight. He leaned down to her and whispered.

"You still haven't told her, have you? You really need to get it over with."

"You're not like my ex," he'd reassured her earlier that morning. "She had no intention of ever changing. She just wanted to spend, spend, spend until she sent us bankrupt. I know how much debt you've got into since you've been on your own, Lucy, but I know you mean to sort it

out. So long as you carry on proving you're taking responsibility, I'll always be right by your side."

During the days of her own spending sprees there was one person Lucy had never dared ask for help – her mum. No matter what, Janice expected her to be a gold-standard daughter with all the accessories included – a beautiful home, a good job, her bank account all in order.

"Mum," Lucy said now, staring over at the chair she'd painted a nice shade of symbolic green. Green for envy, for wanting everything everyone else had, no matter what the price. "Let's go and make a cuppa. I have something to tell you."

Dan kissed her cheek. "You go, girl," he whispered. "I love you – in credit or with your own debt counsellor."

"I wonder if Mum will say the same," she whispered in reply.

He smiled. "Have a little faith, Luce. I'm sure she's realised by now, the things in life that truly make us rich don't cost anything at all." (MW)

MY MAGIC MOMENT...

A robin I'd fed for months finally trusted me enough to land on my hand. It only did so for a brief second, but it was utterly amazing.

Brain Boosters

Missing Link

The answer to each clue is a word which has a link with each of the three words listed.

This word may come at the end (eg **HEAD** linked with **BEACH, BIG, HAMMER**), at the beginning (eg **BLACK** linked with **BEAUTY, BOARD** and **JACK**) or a mixture of the two (eg **STONE** linked with **HAIL, LIME** and **WALL**).

ACROSS

1 Free, Guy, Pit (4)
3 Fish, Rainforest, Storm (8)
8 Cash, Made, Oven (5)
9 Beater, Instrument, Solar (5)
11 Desk, Filing, Town (5)
12 Festival, Moon, Mouse (7)
14 Colour, Forward, Track (4)
16 Group, Life, Pressure (4)
20 Fibre, Illusion, Telescope (7)
22 Away, Full, Over (5)
24 Costume, Queen, School (5)
26 Easy, Heavy, Steady (5)
27 Card, Mistaken, Theft (8)
28 Breeches, Cap, High (4)

DOWN

1 Bread, Polish, Windows (6)
2 Extra, Print, Scale (5)
4 Bio, Natural, Section (6)
5 Back, Waste, Work (5)
6 Do, Opener, Tin (3)
7 Bread, Shopping, Weave (6)
10 Arrival, Developer, Lunch (4)
13 Candy, Evil, Level (3)
15 Abstract, Gallery, Modern (3)
16 Relations, School, Sector (6)
17 Case, Down, Free (4)
18 Attendant, Charter, Path (6)
19 Jet, Room, Search (6)
21 Gold, Ivory, Line (5)
23 Barrel, Donor, Mouth (5)
25 Inspiring, Over, Struck (3)

Turn To
Page 155 For
Solutions

Hidden word in the shaded squares: _____

French Kiss

I was concentrating on the culture and Judith on the language… maybe we both needed to diversify

By Sandra Bancroft

I still get a thrill when I leave the cool of the airport and step out into the dazzling heat of Nice.

The first time was nearly twenty years ago when, as a naïve teenager, I touched down in the Côte d'Azur, ready for adventure, lured by my college lecturer's promise of "immersing yourself in the local language and culture".

That morning, just like today, had been perfect, hot and still, the sun shining down from a deep blue sky.

A bus was waiting to deliver twenty-four over-excited language exchange students to our host families, and I clambered aboard to sit beside my best friend, Judith. The driver navigated his way slowly along the Promenade des Anglais while we checked out the beautiful people strolling along the boulevard.

"They're all so chic. And skinny," wailed Judith.

"A tan always makes you look thinner," I assured her. "A few days of sun-worshipping and you'll knock the socks off them."

"It's all right for you, eating anything and everything you fancy. I just have to think about food and, hey presto, it mysteriously piles on overnight."

She buried herself deeper into the billowing black dress she was wearing.

"I wish you'd stop worrying about your weight." I hugged her. "You're adorable."

But as always, Judith never believed my affectionate assurances.

"You don't have to lie to me." She huffed. "I know I'm fat."

It was on the tip of my tongue to tell her that rather than agonising for months on a futile diet, an easier, and instant, way of transforming her image would be to burn her wardrobe. But luckily for me, the bus driver shouted my name. It was my stop.

Before I climbed down the steps, I turned back to wave au revoir. She gazed at me, eyes huge in her pale face. I sent her an encouraging smile and exited the bus to be warmly welcomed by my host family.

Marc and Carole Aubert were twins, the same age as me, and lived with their parents in an apartment close to the port. They were both studying economics and keen to practise their English.

"We are going to meet some friends. Would you like to join us?"

"Yes – I mean, oui."

I thought I should at least attempt some French.

The café smelled thickly of rich coffee and cigarette smoke. Aimee, Pierre and Luc introduced themselves and pulled two tables together to make room for everyone. We ordered beers and Aimee offered me a cigarette. I accepted, taking my first puff of a Gauloise with what I hoped was a sophisticated flourish.

My new friends bombarded me with endless questions.

"Slower… ralentissez," I protested.

"We will speak English to make conversations easier, yes?" suggested Marc sympathetically. ➡

I nodded in relief, much preferring to immerse myself in the culture rather than the language. I raised my glass.

"Well… cheers."

I caught up with Judith at our official welcome reception at the town hall a couple of days later. I had spent the time playing volleyball on the beach and hanging out at various cafés drinking red wine and beer. And I was by now an experienced smoker.

My hair was streaked blonde by the sun and my tan was deepening to bronze.

Judith, on the other hand, looked terrible. She was wearing a frumpy dress that enveloped her from neck to foot. It couldn't, however, hide her scarlet face which was already starting to show signs of peeling.

"Ouch. That looks sore."

"It's not too bad. I've spent this afternoon on my bed covered in ice packs. What have you been up to?"

I introduced her to Marc and Carole.

"We are going to Monaco tomorrow," said Carole. "Would you care to join us?"

alone. "And when did you start smoking?"

"Judith, I'm having a very nice time, thank you, and I don't need you to be my conscience."

She flinched.

"Judith…"

But she ignored me and spent the rest of the evening chatting to our French hosts. No doubt practising her language skills I thought, sourly.

But there was a tight feeling in the pit of my stomach. I didn't like being at odds with Judith.

She was my best friend. And perhaps, after all, she was my conscience.

The exchange group was due to visit the Matisse museum the following week and I looked forward to seeing Judith and hearing about Cannes. That was, of course, if she had forgiven me.

At first, I didn't see her, and it crossed my mind that she had stayed away. But then I spotted a lone figure dressed in baggy top and trousers studying a painting.

"Hey," I said.

"Can we talk?"

He guided her towards the shop with the determination of a collie herding a sheep

"Merci, mais je ne peux pas…"

"No, no," said Carole. "We speak English. It is much easier."

Judith frowned at me.

"Thank you but I can't. My host family are taking me to Cannes for a few days."

"That's a shame," replied Carole, and offered Judith a cigarette. She shook her head. Carole shrugged and turned to me.

I smiled and lit up, earning me another look from Judith.

"Why are you not practising French?" she hissed at me, the moment we were

"Sure," I said, gesturing to a convenient sofa in the corner of the exhibition hall.

"No, really talk. Can we go back into town and get a coffee or something?"

I hesitated. I had arranged to meet my French friends at the beach.

Judith started to turn away, but I caught her arm. When the chips were down, she was the one who always listened to me, day or night: my latest crush, my broken heart, my dreadful exam marks…

We crossed the garden of olive trees and headed down the hill through the

university campus to the Old Town. The air smelled of lavender and Herbes de Provence, and young men in leather jackets pinned us to walls as they zoomed past on their vélos shouting and laughing with the shopkeepers, elegant girls clinging to their waists.

"What about here?" asked Judith, pointing to a café beside the Eglise Sainte-Rita.

We were crossing the cobbled street when a man with a charming smile approached Judith, chattering and pointing to a display of dresses in a shop window.

Judith replied to the man in French, too fluent and quick for me to follow.

He threw his hands in the air dismissing her words, guiding her to his shop entrance with the determination of a collie herding a reluctant sheep into a pen.

Frustrated at not being able to follow the conversation, I looked on as the vendor picked out a thin cotton dress, poppy-red with a bold yellow print and spaghetti straps to show Judith.

Ah. I'd finally caught up with what was going on. I knew how this exchange would end because Judith would never wear a dress like that.

But the vendor was obviously a master in persuasion for to my utter astonishment Judith stepped into the shop.

With nothing to do but wait, I walked over to the café, ordered two glasses of white wine and sat down.

When she emerged ten minutes later, murmurs of admiration rippled around the small square.

The bright colours of the dress set off her long black hair perfectly. Her face was smooth and tanned, emphasising the blue of her eyes, turning them almost turquoise.

"Well?" She gave a twirl and I realised that I had been gaping like a goldfish.

"Gorgeous."

She handed me her old top and trousers. "You can do the honours."

I chucked them into a nearby bin.

"You wanted to talk."

Judith took a sip of wine and gazed at me, smiling.

"It's not important any more."

And so here we are, back where it all started, where Judith learned to like herself and I grew up.

Marc is picking us up from the airport and as I scan the crowd, I catch my reflection in the glass door. There are a few extra pounds here and there, but the body's not bad for someone middle-aged with two teenage kids.

Judith waves as Marc's Renault draws up beside us. She's wearing a lime-green sundress that follows every lush curve of her body. She's still my best friend.

"Richard, depeche-toi."

"Oui, cherie," I reply, following her with the suitcases.

And my better half. My wife. **MW**

MY MAGIC MOMENT...

Nice, March 2002. Sitting on a bench on Mont Baron, gazing down on sparkling blue sea, feeling the warmth of the sun, the sound of cicadas. Alone. With a book.

The Harvest Season

Texas, 1945. Two friends seize their chance to escape their one-horse town… but what perils await?

By Alison Carter

Judith Raby and Kate Mathis had been friends since birth. Their mothers lived in adjoining houses in a small town in the middle of the Texas panhandle. Four days after Mrs Raby walked weakly out into the sunshine with her first daughter in her arms, Mrs Mathis walked out with hers, less than two days old. That was just after the end of the War in Europe, 1945, when GIs were coming home.

Judy and Kate worked out pretty fast that there wasn't much to be had from their town. They vowed – as they sat at the edge of a field chewing wheat kernels – that they'd make their fortune elsewhere.

"But how?" Kate asked, screwing her eyes up against the sun.

"I'm gonna be the President's wife," Judy said. "You can be a movie star, being the prettier one."

"That's not true," Kate said. "You're so pretty. But you'd be great in the White House, too."

Marrying a President or becoming a movie star turned out to be unlikely careers for girls from the Raby and Mathis families. They were not to be deterred, however, and by the time they were eighteen, and washing clothes for their large families twice a week, they had spotted a possible way to see the world.

"My cousin Job's joined a crew," Kate announced, one day at the beginning of March, 1963.

"A combine crew?" Judy said.

"Yup. It's heading to Oklahoma to start on the harvest at the end of July." They were sitting side-by-side on the long wooden stoop of the town's only store, sharing a soda. "We could do that."

Judy gave a soft laugh. "You're funny."

"Why not?" Kate said. "I heard of a woman over in Skellytown who was starting a female crew."

Judy turned to look at her friend.

"You're not kidding, are you?" she said.

Combine crews spent May, June and July getting in winter wheat, and then August and September on the spring wheat. They usually moved from Texas through Oklahoma to Kansas, Nebraska, Colorado and then into Dakota where there was, the girls learned, an endless supply of work.

They talked about the possibility of ➝

a crew. The sheer distances made their heads spin but they knew they had to try.

"Can't stay here the rest of my life," Kate declared.

"Me neither," Judy agreed.

The Skellytown woman who was starting up an all-female crew was called Missy Hales, and to Kate and Judy she seemed a little screwy.

"She talked all about something called the women's movement," Judy said after she'd tracked Miss Hales down. "I didn't get most of it. The end of segregation, too. She's what they call 'political'."

Political or not, Missy Hayles was offering jobs. She had already got her crew work and accommodation on four farms, ending at Wichita.

"We work for ourselves," she told Kate and Judy. "We are free; we learn."

The freedom bit sounded nice, and the work bit fine. Judy and Kate weren't sure about the learning bit but they signed up, and packed, and went.

Missy Hales turned out to lack both business acumen and manager skills. After four or five farms she had mostly handed over negotiations to her crew, and especially to Kate and Judy.

"We're kinda used to guys on the crews," a farmer would say, with a mocking smile.

"Listen, we know how to harvest," the women would reply.

"Oh sure," the farmer would say. "It's piecework, anyways. As long as you get the wheat in, in good time, I don't mind if you're ladies or koala bears."

That summer was the hottest for decades, and farmers instructed them only to pump water at certain times. The huts were dusty and stuffy. Working conditions were poor, too, and all the women got tired.

"It's not 'cause we're girls," Judy insisted to Kate. They had just arrived on a huge, flat farm south of Beatrice, Nebraska.

"It's 'cause we never get quite enough sleep, and we're always moving," Kate agreed. The one thing they both knew was that they would keep each other going. They had picked each other up after playtime falls when they were six, anointed each other's insect bites, defended each other from dumb bullies in grade school.

There were rival harvest crews making their way north too, and though the countryside was vast, their paths sometimes crossed. None of these other crews had a single female on them.

There were tussles between Missy's crew and a rival outfit, if some greedy farmer worked out that if he let the crews compete, the price of the work might drop. The men found Missy and her team funny, but the jokes got less kind as the season went along.

"Do you cry if the combine breaks down?" some wise guy would call out. "Women get so emotional!"

"You want some pretty pink ribbons for tying them bales?" someone else would ask.

Kate and Judy were disappointed at the quality of the available men. They'd expected a greater choice away from home.

"They're the same as back home," Kate grumbled. "Too many teeth, or not nearly enough teeth."

"Not great at shaving."

"Not great at thinking!"

"No, he doesn't. Missy heard Janice –"

"*Janice?*"

"I know. Who'd have thought it? Missy heard her talking to a grain broker who was travelling through, offering to sell to him on the side. Janice was batting those eyelashes of hers, apparently."

"I bet she was. The miserable little –"

"Look," Judy interrupted, "I'm thinking this is all getting a little too much. It's bad enough, the heat and the bad pay and the latrines, but if the other girls are going to risk our jobs, then I say we maybe do the next farm, the big one that Missy is so pleased we've got, and then

The world was changing for women – screwy Missy had taught them that much

They would fall about laughing, and promise each other that once this harvest season was done they would use the money they'd saved to really travel.

But it wasn't as easy to save as they'd expected. The itinerant life incurred surprising costs, and after endless days in the field they needed to cheer themselves up with trips to whatever basic diner a town offered.

Then Missy discovered that one of the crew had been high-grading. Judy shared the news – she'd heard it in the dinner hut.

"What's high-grading?" Kate asked.

"It means skimming off some of the wheat to sell privately."

Kate stared. "Making dollars on the side? That risks getting us all moved on, surely? Does Grady know?"

Johnnie Grady was the farmer whose wheat fields they'd been working.

Kate looked anxious.

"If he knows, he'll make sure all the farmers northward know, and we'll reach a dead end – no work."

think about going home."

Kate nodded in agreement. The friends thought alike; nearly two decades of friendship had seen to that.

"As long as we're doing this together," she said firmly.

The next morning was a little cooler, and Judy got out of her narrow cot beside Kate's feeling optimistic. The prospect of home, even a home like theirs, felt good after a month of harvest work.

They'd stashed away as many dollars as they could, and after a break back in Texas they'd make their way to Austin or even Dallas, to find something better to do with their lives. The world was changing for women – screwy Missy had taught them that much – and that world was their oyster.

In her cot, Kate began to cough, pretty much still in her sleep. Judy had noticed Kate's cough getting worse, though Kate shrugged it off. Grain dust could really get into the throat, and Kate was thinner ➜

than her friend, so less strong. The cough was another reason why they ought to be headed back to Texas, Judy thought.

She looked at herself in the cracked mirror hanging on the back of the hut door, combed her hair and put it up with a band. Then she took out the only lipstick she owned, scraped out almost the last of it and applied it to her lips. It was a silly thing to do, because that day would be like all the others – seven hours of labour. But change was coming for her and for Kate. She stepped outside, heading for the dinner hut and the possibility of eggs.

"Well, good morning!"

A man in a narrow-brimmed hat was leaning against a wall in the sunshine. The hat was tipped over his eyes, but Judy saw high cheekbones, concave cheeks, a faint smile. His body was bent in a long curve. He was like a narrow six-foot plank awaiting a carpenter, but the overriding the folks, and now I have business round here so I'll be sticking around a while." He smiled a languorous smile. "Pleasure as well as business, I can see."

Owen Grady was charming. The way he looked, and the way he looked at her, had a powerful effect on Judy. Even that morning, in the brief minutes before she had to run for work, she fell under a spell.

"You'll be back at six?" he asked as she hurried off, breakfast-less, to work.

"I guess so," Judy said. It was a dumb reply: where else was she going to be?

Judy met Owen twice over the next couple of evenings. He asked her to come visit him in a copse behind the house, and then to come out with him to a bar over in the nearby town.

"I don't expect my pop would be thrilled to see me getting to know the combiners," he said with his beautiful,

Judy was surprised how soon he tried to kiss her, and how soon he succeeded

impression was of something snake-like.

"Good morning," Judy answered. She felt awkward in her pinafore dress with the checked shirt underneath and the sleeves rolled up.

"I did not believe my pop," said the man in a voice with a hint of a drawl, "when he said he'd hired an all-girl crew for the spring wheat. But he wasn't lying. I take my hat off to him."

The man took his hat off, and pushed his lean body away from the wall. Judy was transfixed; she couldn't shift the image of a snake, drawing in its victim with its eyes.

"I'm Owen Grady."

"Mr Grady's son?"

"I'm back from Omaha. I never did take to farming, but I come back and see reptilian smile. "That said, I've never been minded to, not before this summer."

Judy lay in her cot at night wondering if this was love. It was certainly sudden, and it was definitely overwhelming. But beside her Kate coughed, tossed and turned. Kate had asked where Judy was going when she left the huts, and Judy had said something vague about a walk.

"You stay here," she said to Kate. "Don't go walking in more dust."

Judy was surprised at how soon Owen tried to kiss her, and how soon he succeeded. She was even more surprised at the way he did it, pressing her against a tree in the depths of the woodland, moving from her lips to her neck to her naked shoulder. It felt good, and at the same time too fast. When she got back to the huts Kate was slumped on the stoop.

"You OK?" Judy asked in concern.

"Fine," said Kate, "though I think the idea of stopping this work is kinda making me feel more exhausted – like the way our teacher in fourth grade said she got a cold every time the holidays were coming. She said her health had been holding out 'til then, you know?"

Kate began to cough, and Judy saw how pale she was. Her thinness had always made Kate somehow lovelier: Missy (who'd been to college) said she looked like Ophelia from *Hamlet*, or a water nymph.

But it struck Judy like a bolt to the heart that her friend needed to leave the fields. She, Judy, would have to work hard for both of them until that time, and plan the trip home, and in doing that she'd have to reject Owen.

That thought made the bolt shoot in a little deeper, but it had to be so. Her friendship with Kate was everything; they had started this adventure together, and she must carry on with her part.

Judy told Owen it wasn't going to work out. He was upset: he said he was crazy about her, that he probably loved her. He told her about his success in business, and he tried hard to kiss her again. It took an effort of will for Judy to back away, and go back to see if Kate was all right.

She was. The air had grown cooler over the past few days, and there had been a delivery of oranges, and a day off for Labor Day, and Kate was up and about. It made Judy glad – until, a few days after that – she learned that Owen had taken Kate out.

"He's somethin', aint he?" said one of the other women. "I don't blame either of you, though – he's like a magnet with that lizardy body of his and that smile. If I was ten years younger!"

Judy was flabbergasted. At first she refused to believe it; she checked with other members of the crew, thinking it must have been one of them that had been with Owen. But it was true – Owen had been seen walking with Kate into the same copse, and coming out again laughing and blushing. "With his arm tight round that tiny waist of hers," they said. "She was havin' the time of her life! You gotta admit she deserves it, she's been so lethargic and unwell and all."

Judy sat for what seemed like hours, going over in her mind what Kate could be thinking, what could have possessed her to see Owen, knowing about Judy's feelings for him. To betray her oldest and best friend!

Judy imagined what she would say to Kate. She ran through in her mind the angry accusations, the hurt and disappointment that she would express. Hadn't she given up Owen just so she could make sure Kate got to a better place, and got well?

Missy found Judy in the hut in that afternoon, sitting with her head in her hands. Missy was cannier than Judy had realised, despite Missy's head being forever in the clouds or in a book, and she knew something of what was going on.

"So what's your plan?" Missy asked ➜

in her calm, clever-woman's voice.

"To confront her," Judy said. The prospect seemed satisfying, the opportunity for revenge seductive.

"That'll make you feel good, I guess," Missy said.

"It sure will," Judy replied.

"Will you yell at the guy, too?"

Judy took her head out of her hands. Missy was looking down at her, her expression matter-of-fact. The woman always supported the "sisterhood", always wanted to remind everybody of how great females were in the scheme of things.

"What?" Judy said.

"Just sayin'," Missy replied with a shrug.

Already, Judy felt deflated. The thought of yelling at Kate had lost its gloss. Missy had taken that gloss off, which infuriated Judy. Everything was infuriating.

"I don't know," Judy said, "but I am mad as hell."

"That's natural," Missy said. "Want some supper?"

They moved on that very evening, which meant that Judy did not have to decide how to act. But as they packed up, Judy saw Owen and Kate standing just behind one of the barns, kissing. She wanted not to look, but her eyes wouldn't shift. It was even worse when out came Kate to the trucks, looking shy and flustered. Judy quietly climbed on the second truck. She watched Kate looking around for her, and finally, as the first truck's engine rumbled into life, getting aboard and sitting looking puzzled.

Judy thought that she would save her anger. It would be like a delicious treat that her mother had sometimes packed in her lunch pail, a treat to imagine for hours until you took it out and enjoyed it. There was time for her to tell Kate exactly how wicked she was.

Judy asked Missy to arrange a different hut for her at the next farm, and to put her on a different rota, and in this way she kept out of Kate's way. Kate tried to find her, but it was easier than Judy thought to avoid someone living so close by; it was just that she'd never wanted to before.

"Your friend Kate's looking for you," Missy said on the second evening, but Judy shrugged and said she had things to do.

"I think she's going to the town," Missy continued. "There's a regular dance they hold there – rock and roll. They say it's good fun."

Judy said she didn't dance.

"I guess that guy will come up from Grady's," somebody said, "and dance with Kate – the two of them left it that they had a thing going, I think."

"I guess so. She's welcome to him," Judy said. As she spoke she was remembering Owen's kiss, so practised and so heated, and his hands on her back.

She was angry and confused, and her heart felt as though it had been emptied and hung out to dry. Though when Missy looked at her across the parched field, she wasn't sure if it as the loss of Owen, or – dammit – the loss of Kate.

The rock and roll dance was held twice a week. One of the other women, a cheerful girl called Prudence from Amarillo, persuaded Judy to go along to the next one with her.

"I seen you looking so fumy at your

friend," Prudence said. "In my book, you don't wanna let someone like that get everything that's to be had. Come along and dance. Have a ball and show her you don't care that she stole your man."

It didn't sound like the ball that Prudence suggested it was, but Judy was going crazy in the hot, airless huts, and so she agreed to go.

The dance was held in a hall outside the town, on the open road. As Judy walked in, she smelled shaved wood and root beer, and saw local kids leaning against the walls trying to look nonchalant.

Judy felt like a grown-up, betrayed in both love and friendship. She was nursing real hurt, while this crowd of youngsters jockeyed to get the best-looking partner and show off their conquests.

Judy wondered where Kate was, and

Judy felt a current pass between them.

Then a stocky guy in a lumberjack shirt came over and asked the blonde to dance. She looked at Owen and pouted again, and in her eyes Judy saw the glint of desperation. She wanted Owen to claim her; that was the effect he had on women.

"Look after this one, Chuck," Owen said, and he propelled the blonde onto the dance floor, shoving Chuck after her. A slow song had started on the gramophone, and Judy could hear the conversation between the men who remained. She sipped her soda, trying to look as though she was watching the dancing. Kate was only five feet away, and Judy knew she was doing the same.

"They oughta lock you up, Grady," said a man beside Owen. "Cindy's fallen for you like a stone."

"There's the ones you marry, the ones you date and the ones you do as you like with"

one of the harvest crew said that she had gone to the ladies' room.

Owen Grady, standing with a group in the part of the room furthest from the dance floor, drew looks from every female in the place. His group crossed the room, strolling past Judy to the long trestles, just as Kate came back. They were in a sort of triangle now – Owen, Kate and Judy – though Owen hadn't noticed either of them: his people were clustered round him and his attention was focussed on a tall blonde girl. He was standing with his back to them.

"Get me potato chips, Owen honey!" the blonde said. She pouted, and her voice had a coy, whining quality.

Owen touched the blonde on her lower back, keeping his hand there. Judy and Kate didn't look at each other, but

"You should leave some for the rest of us," said another man with a weak grin.

Kate thought she heard Owen chuckle. He drained a bottle of beer.

"What about the woman you see in Omaha?" his friend asked.

"She's good. She's spending her daddy's money in the stores – hopefully on me. It's my birthday next week."

"You'll marry her, d'you think?"

"Well I'm not going to get myself hitched to one of those," said Owen. He turned through ninety degrees to look at the blonde, indicating her with his thumb.

"But Cindy's a doll," someone said.

"Oh sure," said Owen. "She's good for diversion. She's no use to me, though."

The other men looked at each other, their faces half shocked, half admiring.

"You gotta divide women up ➤

appropriately, boys," Owen said with a swagger. "There's the ones you marry, the ones you date, and finally the ones you do just as you like with – the ones just passing through."

"Them harvest girls?"

"There's only a couple worth the trouble," Owen said. "You can play 'em off against each other for added interest, too, if you got the energy. Say, can anyone get me another beer? I don't know why I'm the one providing all the learnin' here."

Judy backed away from the men at exactly the same moment as Kate. They almost got stuck in the doorway, trying to get outside, and in ten seconds they were breathing hard in the evening air. Then the explanations began.

"He said you didn't like him," Kate said. "He told me that he asked you out to get close to me." Tears were in her eyes. "He said he loved me."

"You too?" Judy said.

She told Kate why she'd rejected Owen – so they could move on and get home – and Kate was horrified. She said she was sorry, that Owen had told a dozen lies.

"He's not interested in either of us," Judy said, "except as another scalp."

"And you were thinking of me all the time?" Kate said.

They heard a burst of male laughter and looked behind them through the long windows of the dance room. Owen and his buddies had moved into the centre of the room, and Owen was preparing to dance with a young and eager girl in a bright red skirt with too many petticoats. He ran a hand slowly through his dark hair and glanced round the room.

"He's vain," Kate said.

"How did I not see that?"

"He's like a snake."

"A venomous snake, not a cute one. Let's go back."

It was a long walk back to the farm – maybe three miles – but the road was straight and the night young. The wheat fields glowed yellow and gold in the declining sun.

"We've seen off a lot together, Katie," Judy remarked as they walked.

"Chicken pox," Kate agreed, "and your grandma being so ill that time. Math tests."

"We shared the answers and we still only got a C!"

They laughed.

"Now we've seen off a tough harvesting job," Judy went on, "and rotten food and bad pay."

"Missy's lectures about feminism."

Judy stopped walking.

"Missy knows more than you'd think. Not about taxes and managing farmers, but about how to be a female, I think."

Kate took Judy's hand. "Can you believe we almost let a guy break us, after all we've been through together? A guy?"

"It was crazy," said Judy. "It was a close shave."

The high, cutting song of a savannah sparrow reached them in the warm air.

"There's a lesson," Judy said. "We'll never let anybody hurt what we have."

"Trust," Kate murmured softly. "It's all about trust."

They walked on, and their movement – just two tiny figures in a great flat landscape – seemed to cause a breeze. It made the wheat move in waves, rippling as the sun set behind it. **MW**

....

MY MAGIC MOMENT...

I was 21, about to start my dream job, boating on a dark blue Mediterranean at sunset. A shoal of dolphins appeared and followed us into harbour. I recognised that life doesn't get much better!

Celebration Time

Pizza Scones

Ingredients (Makes 16)

- ◆ **500g self-raising flour**
- ◆ **10g baking powder**
- ◆ **100g butter or margarine, cut into small pieces**
- ◆ **100g sundried tomatoes, drained**
- ◆ **125g pitted black olives, drained**
- ◆ **100g freshly grated Parmesan cheese**
- ◆ **2 medium eggs, beaten**
- ◆ **Approx 210ml whole milk**
- ◆ **100g mature Cheddar cheese, grated**
- ◆ **100g frozen sliced peppers**

1 Preheat the oven to 200°C, Fan Oven 180°C, Gas Mark 6. Line 2 baking trays with baking parchment. Put flour, baking powder and butter in a large bowl and rub together with your fingertips.

2 Blot tomatoes well on kitchen paper and chop. Cut 8 olives in half and put to one side. Chop the rest and stir into the flour mix with the tomatoes and Parmesan. Make a well in the centre, add eggs and gradually stir in sufficient milk to form a soft dough. On a floured surface, knead gently until smooth.

3 Divide the dough in half. Form each into an 18cm round and place on the baking trays. Score the tops into 8 equal portions and bake for 20min. Sprinkle with Cheddar, peppers and olive halves, and bake for a further 20min until risen and golden. Cool on a wire rack then cut into wedges. ➜ **P 127**

RECIPE AND FOOD STYLING: KATHRYN HAWKINS PHOTOGRAPHY: STUART MACGREGOR

For The Love Of Fred

In a roundabout way, Emma's love of gardening had the power to make lots of people very happy…

By Pippa Newnton

Sue lived on the second floor of a block of flats just outside the town of Crampton. Her windows overlooked a roundabout filled with shrubs, plants and flowers with a tree in the middle.

Sue loved the greenery – bulbs in the spring, flowers in the summer, and coloured foliage in the autumn. She was sure that it also gladdened the hearts of those who drove round it on their way to work every day.

The roundabout was tended with loving care by Emma Townsend, an elderly lady who carried a gardening trug, a trowel, shears and a watering

from a detached house that had been too big for them when the children left home.

Emma was a keen gardener and their house had a large garden which they had both tended with loving care, but the flats had no garden.

When her husband died a year ago, Emma felt that the bottom had dropped out of her life. In her grief, she noticed that the roundabout opposite the flats had become weed-filled and neglected. This gave her an idea, and a purpose in life.

Without asking the council, she took the law into her own hands, deciding to treat the roundabout as her garden. She made a wonderful job of it and people often remarked on how well it looked.

"You mean they are going to bulldoze all those lovely flowers and shrubs?"

can across to her plot every morning.

Emma lived on the ground floor of the same flats as Sue. Their paths would cross when she came back from her gardening expedition and Sue came down ready to go to work in the local supermarket.

They always stopped for a chat and Sue learned that Emma had moved into the ground floor flat with her husband Fred three years ago. They had downsized

And then came the blow…

Sue's sweetheart, Ted Stokes, was an assistant in the planning department of the council.

One evening when Ted and Sue were having a drink in the Crampton Arms, she sensed Ted had something on his mind.

He's going to propose to me! she thought excitedly.

He leaned across the table and held

her hand in his. Her heart fluttered.

"I'm sorry to tell you this," he said.

Oh, no, he's going to leave me! Sue's heart sank.

Then to her surprise he said, "I know how much you care for the roundabout outside your flats but it's going to be levelled and replaced by a small disc."

Sue was aghast.

"You mean they are going to bulldoze all those lovely shrubs and flowers?"

"That's about the size of it. Much neater, though, don't you think?"

Sue leaned towards him, her eyes flashing with anger.

"That roundabout is a thing of beauty. Not only do motorists get pleasure in driving round it, but the view from our flats is simply stunning. And what about Emma Townsend?" ➜

"Emma Townsend?" Ted looked puzzled. "What's she got to do with it?"

"You mean you don't know?"

"No – what?"

"She looks after all those plants on the roundabout."

"I didn't know we employed anyone to do that."

"You don't. She does it out of love. If you destroy the roundabout, you destroy everything she lives for."

"Well, that's the Council's decision so there we are!"

"That's a heartless thing to say." Sue got up, finished her drink and mumbled that she had to go. She loved Ted, but that remark was so out of character that she felt churned up inside.

When she got home she burst into tears and had a restless night with dreams of bulldozers tearing up the plants and levelling the roundabout.

She recovered a bit next morning when Ted phoned her early.

felt good – but how could she prevent the council from carrying out their plan?

The council offices were situated in a grand building halfway up the high street, set in a gated garden full of plants and flowers. She had never been before, but it would be interesting to see where Ted worked.

She went through the double glass doors and on to the reception desk, where a large woman in a green dress embroidered with the caption *Crampton Council* looked up fiercely.

Oh dear, Sue thought.

Then to her surprise the woman asked, "Can I help you?" in a very pleasant voice.

It was such a contrast to her looks that Sue was taken aback for a moment.

"Can you direct me to the department that wrecks roundabouts?" she asked.

The woman turned automatically to her screen and was about to tap some keys but turned and smiled. "I'm sorry we don't have such a department."

"I told you I mustn't be disturbed –" He put down his pen. "Who are you?"

"I'm sorry if I upset you," he said, "but council decisions are final. I don't know what we could do about it."

"It's nice of you to say 'we' but I can't let this happen. It means such a lot to Emma." Sue looked out of her window and saw Emma crossing the road to the roundabout. "I'm on late shift today. I'll come round to the council offices and try to see someone about it."

The air was fresh with the smell of honeysuckle as she walked past the roundabout, waving to Emma. It was a glorious day, with small fluffy clouds sailing serenely across the blue sky. She

"Well, I've just heard that the council are going to destroy the roundabout just out of town. Can you give me the name of the person who ordered the destroying?"

For a moment the receptionist looked helpless. Then she had an idea.

"You could try the planning department, I suppose. They may be able to help you."

"It's a start. Where do I go?"

Sue thought it best not to mention that she had a friend in the department.

"Oh, you can't go up there without an appointment. Mr Phipps, the planning officer, is very strict about that." She pulled out a large diary from a drawer.

"Would next Tuesday suit you at all?"

"No, it wouldn't," Sue pushed past the desk and through the door on the left of the reception area.

"Wait, no, don't." The woman half rose from her seat, but Sue was gone.

She found herself in a long corridor with doors on either side. She walked purposefully along looking at names on the doors until she came to one labelled *Planning*.

She stopped and looked through the glass. There was a small girl sitting at a desk, and there was Ted taking something out of a filing cabinet. She went in.

"Can I help you?" the girl asked.

"It's all right, Mavis, this is a friend of mine." Ted smiled, " Sue – I knew you'd think of something."

"I'm not sure that I have but I've come to see your Mr Phipps." She pointed to a door on the far wall with the name *Adrian Phipps, Planning Officer* on it.

"Oh, but you really need an appointment –" Ted began.

"No, I don't."

Sue walked boldly across the room, knocked on the door and went in.

She saw a large man, red-faced and balding, sitting at a large mahogany desk, looking down at a mass of papers, a worried look on his face. He looked up.

"I told you I mustn't be disturbed –" He put down his pen. "Oh – who are you?"

Adrian Phipps saw before him a slim, good-looking girl dressed smartly in a white blouse and tapered blue slacks.

"I'm sorry to disturb you," Sue said. "I'm Sue Ellis and I've come about the roundabout that your people are planning to destroy."

"That's not my department," he looked irritated. "Go away."

Sue stood firmly in front of him.

"This is important."

Adrian Phipps gave a sigh, pushing the stack of papers to the front of his desk.

"Sit down, young lady. I can spare you five minutes. Now, what's this all about?"

Sue put the case for the roundabout and Emma as simply as she could.

Adrian Phipps leaned back in his chair, tapping his teeth with his pen.

"I know the roundabout and I can see your point," he said. "Unfortunately it isn't up to me. It may be being dealt with by either transport or leisure and recreation. Your best bet is to get ten people to support you in a petition and send it to us. Then it will have to be considered in a meeting of the council."

Sue calmed down a bit.

"That would very helpful if we had time," she said, "but by the time that happens they will have gone ahead and destroyed the roundabout."

"I'm sorry, Miss Ellis. That's the best I can do for you. Now I must get back to work." She turned to go and he added with a twinkle in his eye, "Of course you could chain yourself to the tree on the roundabout if you felt so strongly about it."

As she went out, Ted was still standing clutching the file he had taken out of the filing cabinet as she went in.

"What happened in there?" he asked her, wide-eyed at her daring.

"He told me to chain myself to the roundabout. Nothing helpful."

"Sorry about that – but he is really a very nice person."

That evening Ted explained that ➤

Mr Phipps had been involved in a complex planning application.

"He was very worried about it and I'm surprised he agreed to talk to you at all."

Ted rang her up next day at the supermarket, a thing he never did. Her supervisor called her over, looking on disapprovingly while she took the call.

"Sue," Ted said. "Mr Phipps has asked you to come round after work if you can."

"I finish at three. What can he want?"

"I don't know. He just asked you to come in. Shall I tell him you'll be here?"

"Yes. I must go now as we're not supposed to take calls in work time."

She put the phone down and said to the supervisor, "That was the council. I have to go in for a meeting."

"That's fine – but remember, in future, no phone calls at work,"

At around four o'clock she presented herself at the council offices where Ted took her to Mr Phipps' office.

"I'm sorry I was so occupied when you first visited," he told her. "Afterwards I gave it some thought and decided that perhaps we could do something for you." Adrian Phipps smiled. "I checked who gave the order to level the roundabout and found it had been delegated to a junior officer in the transport office. I've changed the decision. Your roundabout is safe."

Smiling at her gasp of delight, he went on, "There are two other roundabouts outside town. They are supposed to be maintained by the firms that sponsor them but I've spoken to their representatives and we have agreed to pay Mrs Townsend to keep all three up to scratch."

"That's fantastic news." Sue almost leaned over the desk and hugged him. "I can't wait to tell Emma."

Adrian smiled, "we've already had her in and she has agreed to do it. It won't be easy, but the roundabouts will be a credit to the town and she'll be kept busy."

A weekend or two later Sue and Ted were out for a walk.

"I want to show you something." Sue led him across the road and on to the roundabout. There, nestling under the tree, surrounded by flowers, was a brand new bench with a small plaque.

"Look what Emma has done. Come and sit down."

As he sat, he turned round and read the inscription, *To the memory of a loving husband, Fred Townsend.*

"As soon as she knew she was the official roundabout gardener, she got permission to buy this bench and put it under the tree." Sue patted the seat.

"That's a lovely thought," Ted said, "but why are all these benches dedicated to dead people? Why not have one dedicated to the living?" Dropping to his knees, he grasped her hand. "How about another roundabout seat dedicated to Mr and Mrs Sue and Ted Stokes?" **MW**

MY MAGIC MOMENT...

On a holiday in Cornwall, the local bank was closing, and the two assistants risked losing their jobs. It inspired my story about one of them becoming a lifeboat volunteer. My Weekly published it. My first published story!

Most Uplifting Historical Events

✦ Beatlemania arrived in America at JFK airport in New York in 1964!

✦ The Wright Brothers' first flight in 1903 marked a revolution in human transport.

✦ In 1927, Charels Londenbergh achieved the world's first non-stop transatlantic flight.

✦ On March 2, 1969, the Anglo-French supersonic Concorde made its first flight.

✦ On July 21, 1969, Neil Armstrong was the first man to foot on the Moon.

✦ On November 9, 1989, the Berlin Wall was breached after nearly three decades of dividing east and West Berlin.

✦ On February 11, 1990, Nelson Mandela was released after 27 years of imprisonment in Victor Verster prison.

✦ Newly divorced and struggling to make ends meet, single mum Joanne Rowling published her first Harry Potter novel in 1997, inspiring a whole new generation of readers and shattering sales records.

✦ Apple unveiled the iPhone in 2007, bringing about the "Touch Revolution" that rocked the software world.

✦ Harriet Tubman, the former slave and abolitionist who led hundreds of slaves to freedom, was featured on the new $20 bills in 2016.

✦ On May 6, 1954, Roger Bannister was the first man to break the four-minute mile.

✦ Soviet cosmonaut Yuri Gagarin became the first man in space after completing an orbit of Earth in his Vostok spacecraft in 1961.

Barack Obama was elected as the first black President of America in 2008

✦ Emily Davison, by throwing herself under the King's horse in 1913, gave the Suffragette movement the impetus it needed and she changed the lives of ordinary women.

Under The Apple Tree

Back then, he made everything magical for me – and that magic has never faded over the years

By Lynda Franklin

It's funny how one moment in a single day can suddenly send you reeling back in time so fast it's hard to catch your breath. One beautiful sweet-smelling moment, one cloudless sky, and the years simply roll away.

I close my eyes for that moment. It's easy to float back in time, like a cloud bobbing through the decades until it comes to rest on a day so special in my mind I can't bear to leave it. I'm back under the yellow umbrella.

I was Lottie then, not Charlotte. A small, trusting little Lottie in a world full of

showers that day, the sky the colour of creamy yogurt, and we sat on the grass under a bright yellow umbrella.

I remember sticking my legs out from underneath so I could feel the raindrops on my legs between my raincoat and wellies, leaning closely into him.

He was back, and although I didn't know for how long, the pure joy of being with him overwhelmed me. The grown-ups said he would have to go again soon.

Some grown-ups worked in shops and banks and offices, but mine had to go away. I wasn't quite sure where he went, or what he did, but I was certain he would always come back.

When he was with me, I pushed reality away. The present was all that mattered

miracles. I remember being scared, not wanting to let the tiny pip go, holding it tightly in my hand, safely against my body, nursing it like a small baby.

Only reluctantly did I finally drop it into the earth, watching carefully where it fell, my small hands coaxed into covering it gently with mud. The earth felt damp and stuck to my fingers, and he wiped them clean with a handkerchief.

The sun was shining through the

So I waited. I waited with a longing no one could have imagined, hugging it to myself, possessive of our time together and the total love he gave me on his return.

I knew I would have him for only a short time, but when he was with me I pushed reality away. The present was all that mattered. The moment. The precious golden hours spent with him.

I worried about the tiny pip we'd buried together, fearing for it under the earth, ➤

covered in blackness. I was scared of the dark – surely only bad things happened when it was dark.

I wanted our seed to feel the delicious warmth that came with every summer, every picnic, every longed-for ice cream. I willed it to leave the earth behind, push for the sunshine and soft fresh air above and burst into branches and leaves and beautiful apples.

My brightest memories were soaked in sunny showers and carefree, never-ending days. There must have been others, but not important enough to be stored and treasured. Nothing should be left alone in scary, damp, dark mud. That's what I told him under the yellow umbrella.

My father had smiled then. He was wearing blue slacks and a short-sleeved shirt open at the neck.

"You have to be patient," he told me, covering my fingers with his. His hand felt big on mine, and I loved the feel of his roughened skin against my softness.

I knew how to be patient. Didn't I wait patiently for him to return every time?

Sky People bouncing across clouds and fairies that lived in rainbows. Vivid stories that made me yearn to fly and play in the magical playground above me. Tales that made me feel I could sit on a star and ride the crest of moon beams.

He put his arms around me and held me tight, and my mind was full of wonder as I listened mesmerised under the yellow umbrella. The stories stayed in my head always, easing the separation, firing my imagination until I believed I really knew those enchanted people who inhabited that mysterious space above our heads.

"Everyone needs to reach for the sky. That's where all the best dreams are kept," he told me.

"Will I reach the sky one day?" I asked.

His bronzed face relaxed into a smile, and I remember playing with strands of his brown hair waving in the breeze, wanting to memorise every detail of his face before he went away.

"Oh, I hope so, little one," he murmured.

"Will you be with me?"

I pull one of my first crop from the tree. It coats my mouth in delicious sweetness

I will never forget the day I saw a thin shoot clawing its way from the ground. I ran to him and we danced, holding hands and laughing together. Then we lay on the scratchy grass side by side, me staring at the spindly shoot, afraid to take my eyes off it. Why couldn't I see more shoots, more leaves, the beginnings of an apple? Where were all the apples?

"You must be patient, Lottie." He laughed gently again.

Then he sat up and squatted beside me, pointing out animals in fluffy cloud shapes above us, making up magical stories about

"When you aim for the sky and strive for your dreams? Oh yes, I'll be there all right, Lottie."

"We can sit on a rainbow, can't we?"

"We won't sit, Lottie, we'll dance!"

"And sing?"

"Of course! Rainbows are the best places for singing."

I remember giggling, half understanding that maybe that wouldn't happen, but somehow believing all he told me. He'd promised to be with me. That's all that mattered. I could do anything if he was with me.

I'm Charlotte now. I have a husband, four grown-up children and a sensible grown-up house. Lottie doesn't quite suit me any more. She belongs to a different time, another world, a beautiful place called childhood.

It's late afternoon, and I drag myself back to the present. From my back door I can see the orchard bursting with fruit-laden trees. I call it an orchard, but really it's just my garden. The garden that I planted with apple trees when we first moved in.

Because apple trees mean happiness. Apple trees mean love.

I notice my hands are prematurely aged by gardening, but how I love the feel of rich soil. I pull one of my first crop from the tree. Firm, mottled red, and when I take a bite, it coats my mouth in delicious, sweet crispness. The blight I'd been afraid of hasn't happened.

Satisfied, I slip on a cardigan. The summer still has to warm up a bit, though the sky is blue and the scant clouds crisp and white. I must remember to tell him to put on a jacket. I glance at my watch – it's time I left.

He's waiting for me, and I wish I could run to him as I used to, feel him lift me high and spin me round. Instead I wave, walk more quickly, break into a smile. I can't wait to show him what's happening in my garden, pick an apple from our seed tree, and place it in his hand.

I know exactly what he will do. He'll turn it over in his hand, inhale its aroma briefly, then bite into it. And even though his mind is slowed by age now, his eyesight almost gone, the sweetness and smell of apples will make him smile.

I will describe the orchard to him, the trees bent low with lush, ripe fruit, some still waiting to ripen in the summer sun. And this time he will listen to my stories, and picture the miracle of leafy trees bursting into fruit, filling the orchard with unbelievable scent.

I will make it come alive for him. I will paint such vivid pictures, his imagination will soar as mine did all those years ago.

And I'll remind him of that sunny, showery day under a creamy yogurt sky when we planted our very first seed. He will chuckle and I'll glimpse just for a moment that same look, the sense of wonder and joy he passed on to me.

Then we'll sit under the yellow umbrella, faded now, sipping apple juice on soft-backed chairs. No scratchy grass. No spindly brown legs in wellies.

"It's been a lovely day, Lottie," he'll say, because he always tells me that.

"It has, Dad," I'll say, slipping my arm through his as we sit, making sure he can't go anywhere, can't leave and slip away from me. Even though I know he won't any more.

"Nothing like the smell or taste of apples, Lottie love. Finest thing on God's earth."

And I'll lean against him, feeling the love that still flows like an artery between us. ⓂⓌ

....

MY MAGIC MOMENT...

A wonderful surprise holiday in Devon with my husband, son and three daughters, their partners and all of our eleven grandchildren. How I love the times we are altogether as a family. Perfect.

Say It With Roses

Adam had set out with such high hopes. Now it looked as if he would never get to hand over his bouquet…

By Linda Mitchelmore

H e was feeling an idiot now! Adam had been dead on time for his lunch date with Hannah, but now he'd been standing outside Bailey's for twenty minutes and she hadn't turned up.

The roses he'd brought her – well, OK, stolen because he hadn't asked if he could have them – from his mother's garden were hanging behind his back.

He didn't think passers-by could see them, but he got the feeling they knew he'd been stood up because more than a few had made eye contact and then looked away, embarrassed. One bloke had even mouthed, "Sorry, mate".

Adam hadn't thought to take flowers. It had been his mother's idea when he'd popped in quickly with a new kettle she'd asked him to get her.

"A date, darling!" she'd said, her eyes gleaming. "How lovely."

The sub-text of that was, *and about time too,* although neither of them actually said the words.

"Yes. And I hope it will be. Lovely."

"What's her name?"

"Hannah."

"Oh, super-lovely. I always think Hannah is such a gentle, *organised* sort of name. Hannahs are always capable in my mind. Quite a few of my carers have been Hannahs. You are taking her flowers, darling, aren't you?"

"Um…"

"I know that 'um'. It hadn't crossed your mind, had it? Your father was just the same about flowers. And, well, gifts in general. It was one of the reasons we got divorced."

Adam hadn't been at all sure he was keen on the direction this conversation was going. It was a first date he was on, for goodness' sake. He hadn't thought for a second about marriage – and he would have bet his DVD collection that Hannah hadn't either.

"Any particular type of flower, Mum?" he'd asked. "Just so I avoid, you know, the divorce scenario."

"Roses are always good," his mother replied, whippet-fast. His sarcasm, it seemed, was lost on her, carried away as she seemed to be on a cloud of romance. "Not red on a first date. Give them a good sniff, whatever colour you choose, before you pay for them because so many have no scent these days."

"Right. Roses. Not red. Scented."

"And in clear Cellophane. And make sure there are no thorns."

Adam sent up a silent prayer that the roses in buckets of water outside the corner papershop would be thornless and in clear Cellophane.

He glanced at the kitchen clock. His mother saw the glance, swift as it was.

"And remember, flowers have a magic all of their own and, I think, roses do in particular. Now hurry along, or you'll be late," she said brightly.

Adam considered asking if she thought he was four, or thirty-four. But he knew the answer to that – he would forever be her little boy. And she'd forever be the mum who had three jobs when he was little to keep a roof over their heads and food on the table, after his feckless ➜

father left. Well, she'd had three jobs before she was involved in a bus accident that put her in a wheelchair when Adam had been twenty-three and just finishing university.

It had taken a long time to get the right sort of care for his mother and until he had, he'd been the one to do it. But now that care was well in place and Adam was free to go dating.

Or not, he thought, the roses still dangling behind his back. Chatting with his mother had made him late so he'd picked a dozen yellow roses, mostly in fat bud, from her garden on his way out.

Now he was a partner in a firm of architects, Adam had the wherewithal to pay a gardener to come in once a week and do the garden for her. There'd been no opportunity for buying clear Cellophane but he had at least picked off all the thorns. A quick nip to the garden shed and he found a piece of clean, green twine and fashioned it in a sort of bow.

I wish he wouldn't leave me dangling like this. It's a myth that flowers have to be held with their heads down – they suck up water, for goodness' sake. All it's doing, this dangling thing, is loosening my petals and a leaf has just dropped off.

Adam jiggled his fingers to check the flowers were still there because his hands were going a bit numb now holding them. They were. But there was still no Hannah.

Adam was surprised rather than upset that she wasn't showing. He'd give her another fifteen minutes and then go.

He knew Hannah wasn't the best at technology because it was through technology – in the mobile phone shop – that they'd met. Adam had been updating his and Hannah had been, well, moving from what looked like an extremely ancient pay-as-you go mobile to one with a contract and internet connection.

Perhaps, he thought, *she hasn't mastered how to check the time on her new phone yet.*

It was that simple thing that had confused her. Hannah had left the shop before him but had been outside, propped up against the sill of the display window, a worried frown on her beautiful, heart-shaped face. Her hazel eyes had darkened, and there were little worry lines on her forehead, from which she kept pushing back her deep red curls.

"Oh, Lordy," he heard her mumble. "What did the man say? I can't go back and ask. He'll think I'm an idiot. I only want to know the time!"

"Can I help?" Adam said.

She looked up at him, puzzled.

"Help what?"

"Help you to find the time on your phone. And for the record, I don't think you're an idiot at all."

"Oh!" she said, flustered. "Was I talking out loud?"

"Loud enough for me to hear," Adam said. "But then I've often been told I've got ears like radar. I was in the shop beside you just now and I know your phone's new. So, to repeat… can I help?"

"How long have you got?"

"How long do you need?"

"Oh God, years probably. I'm so out of my comfort zone here. I mean, I can't find the time on this thing, it's so not like my old one, and I have no idea how to go about putting anyone's number in."

"There's a café over there," Adam said. "We could sit outside and I'll give you a few basic lessons."

too long on sorting this phone and…"

"It's OK. I'm not putting you under any obligation. I just thought I'd like to sit opposite you, have lunch with you, when you're not staring at the screen – although I realise that's the purpose of the exercise at the moment."

"And I'd like to have lunch with you," Hannah said, looking at him as though she was seeing him for the first time – which in a way she was, now she wasn't concentrating on her phone. She gave him a smile that almost made his bones melt. "Are you free on Saturdays?"

"This coming Saturday?"

"The very one." Hannah laughed.

And now the very one had come and

She gave a smile that almost made his bones melt. "Are you free on Saturdays?"

So that was what they'd done. They'd exchanged names and Adam had suggested she put his number in first and then ring it to see if she'd done it properly. She had, and she giggled deliciously when Adam answered it and said, "Hi, Hannah".

He'd resisted the urge to save her number although, had he been a betting man, he would have bet she wouldn't have a clue that he had.

"I don't know how to thank you," Hannah had said.

"You could have lunch with me," Adam had said. "Now. In Bailey's. Do you know it? It's just up the road…"

"Oh, I know it – but I can't do that *now*," Hannah had said, flushing, and Adam's heart leapt at the thought that the way she said it suggested she would like to do it some other time. "I've got a million things I should be doing. This isn't a brush-off, by the way, there really are a million things and I've spent far

Hannah hadn't turned up. Another fifteen minutes had gone by. She wasn't coming now. Adam wished he'd saved her number and then he could have rung her to ask if she was running late, or had forgotten – but that would have been almost like stalking, wouldn't it? And Adam wouldn't go there.

Oh dear," Maggie puffed under her breath. "I had no idea it was so far."

Maggie was on her way to visit a neighbour in hospital. She'd come by train and although she'd been told it was just a ten-minute walk to the hospital, it had taken her fifteen minutes already and there was a way to go yet.

It might have helped if she'd been carrying less weight about her person but she couldn't deal with that at the moment. What she'd give for a cup of tea and a Chelsea bun right now, though.

Her neighbour in the block of flats →

she lived in – Annie – had few relatives and Maggie had been told none had visited, so she'd taken it upon herself to fill the gap. Annie had helped Maggie out when she'd broken her wrist; prepping veg for her, doing a bit of mending, and she'd even called a taxi to take them both to Bojangles for coffee.

Ah, a bench. A quick sit down wouldn't hurt, would it? It wasn't even the start of visiting time yet. Maggie plonked herself down in the middle.

Oh. Flowers. Roses. Yellow ones. On the end of the bench. Maggie could smell their spicy, heady scent from where she sat. Garden roses by the look of it, tied with garden twine. She pictured an elderly man who loved his garden picking them

Annie a packet of shortcake biscuits – her favourite – but a few flowers wouldn't go amiss, even though she felt a bit of a cheapskate even thinking of taking these yellow roses. She knew what Annie would say – "Whose garden did you nick these from then, Mags?" And then she'd cackle and Maggie would laugh with her.

Oh, how she hoped Annie would get her sense of humour and her cackle back along with her health. But it felt almost like stealing as Maggie picked them up and held them to her nose.

"Oh, you smell divine," she said, inhaling the roses' perfume. "I wonder what sort you are."

I am so glad you appreciate me. And I'm Graham Thomas. Men can do

Maybe the roses had worked some sort of magic to take her tiredness away…

for a lady. Maybe he was a widower? Perhaps the lady was a widow?

Maggie wondered what might have gone wrong with the giving and receiving of these very lovely yellow roses. She looked around to see if there was anyone nearby who might be coming back for the roses any moment.

No, she didn't think so. There were a few groups of lads joshing about the way lads do, and some girls in too-short skirts – well, Maggie thought they were too short – giggling and showing one another their brightly painted fingernails. An old couple, holding onto one another for support, made their way carefully over the paved shopping precinct but they didn't give the roses a second glance. A few young men in business suits scurried past, mobile phones glued to their ears.

Maggie sidled along the bench until she reached the flowers. She'd brought

fragrance too, you know. But if I'm left here much longer there'll be nothing left of me to appreciate – I'm wilting in this heat. The chap who stole me from his mother's garden was very cavalier in his care of me, I have to say, swinging me about behind his back the way he did.

"I'm going to have to get you into some water soon," Maggie said. The hospital probably had thousands of vases in cupboards somewhere.

"Right then, my lovelies," she said to the roses, suddenly not tired any more. Maybe the roses had worked some sort of magic through their beautiful colour and their perfume to take her tiredness clean away? "Off we go."

I'm sorry, madam," Phil on reception said, "really sorry, but we don't allow flowers by bedsides in this hospital."

He wished he had a ten-pound note for

every time he'd said that. He hated saying it. People had obviously spent good money on flowers for the patients they were visiting and he knew it was a huge disappointment to most that they couldn't hand them over and see the look of pleasure on the recipient's face.

Some left them with him on the desk while they visited their friend or relative and then picked them up again on the way out. But many just left them behind. Or they said, "You have them. Take them home to the wife."

Phil didn't have a wife. He had a husband – Paul. And Paul got hay fever like you wouldn't believe, so he couldn't take them home, much as he loved flowers himself. He wouldn't have minded taking these home – they smelled exquisite. And yellow was Phil's absolute favourite colour.

"No flowers?" the large, very hot-looking lady standing on the other side of the desk repeated. She looked crestfallen.

Phil explained about patients who might have hay fever, or other allergies, and flies and the like that might come in on flowers and then crawl over patients and spread disease or bite and set up infections.

"I hadn't thought of that," the woman said, shamefaced.

"You can leave them here if you like and then pick them up on the way out. I'll put them under the desk with the others that have come in today."

There were already three bunches of flowers and a potted plant sitting under Phil's desk.

Well, thank you very much. I like to choose the company I keep. But at least it will be dark and no more petals will fall off now they don't have the sun on them. I might last a bit longer until someone comes along to take better care of me.

"Confession time," the lady said. "I didn't buy them. I found them."

"Stealing by finding, eh?" Phil said. "It's cuttings that it's OK to steal when no one's looking, because stolen cuttings always take better."

Phil held out his hands to receive the roses and the lady gave them to him.

"I've got a long and probably hot journey home and they'd be dead by the time I get there," she said. "So, you have them. Take them…"

"…Home to the wife," Phil finished for her, good-naturedly enough.

Goodness, but these roses did smell heavenly. They completely masked the hospital smell in the foyer. Well almost.

Hey! Hannah!" Oh, no. Phil on reception was calling her. What did he want? She didn't have time to stop and talk to Phil today, as much as she enjoyed their chats when she did have time. And she'd had a lot of that in the time since she'd broken up with Colm, two years ago.

Phil had been a shoulder to cry on, on more than a few occasions back then. She couldn't ignore whatever it was ➤

that he was wanting her for now…

"Oh, hi," she said, rushing over to his desk. "Did you want something? Only I'm in a bit of a hurry. Late, you know. I had a lunch date but…"

"Don't tell me," Phil said. "There was a patient you just couldn't leave so you've overshot your shift."

"Got it in one. Frank. Ninety-two. He was hanging on, I think, until his granddaughter turned up but she'd been held up. I stayed until she got here."

Once Frank's granddaughter had arrived Hannah had rushed to the staff room, changed out of her uniform and into her best jeans and the jade, silky top she'd brought with her ready to go and meet Adam. She'd fashioned her hair into

"You're not late, Hannah. We can just call it re-scheduled if you like…"

a wispy bun on top of her head and found a lipstick in the bottom of her bag – no make-up allowed on the wards – to give herself a bit of colour after such a sad morning.

And now she was almost an hour late. He wouldn't have waited, would he? She hadn't been able to phone him – no private phones while on duty – but she wished now that she'd been able to.

There had been a connection between her and Adam, she knew it. Something totally different to how she'd felt about Colm, even at the beginning. She'd surprised herself – no, shocked would be more the word – that she'd suggested this Saturday when Adam had suggested lunch. This would be her first real date since her break-up with Colm.

Everyone said it took two years to get over a broken heart, didn't they? But now it was probably all going to be

over before it had even started.

"So," Phil said. "Who's the poor guy you've stood up?"

"I haven't stood him up. Well, not intentionally."

She could ring and explain and maybe they could re-schedule, her and Adam. But she had a gut feeling Adam wouldn't give up easily. He might still be hanging around outside Baileys. If she ran…

"Sorry, Phil, did you want something? Only I've really, really got to go."

"I only wanted to give you these flowers, Han," Phil said, pulling out a bunch of yellow roses from under his desk. Hannah had often been on the receiving end of flowers that visitors had failed to pick up again after visiting. "They've got a fantastic scent."

But fading the longer I'm left out of water. Just get on with it, man, and give me to this beautiful lady.

"Gosh, don't they!" Hannah said rapturously, taking the roses and holding them to her nose. At least, if Adam wasn't anywhere near Bailey's she'd have these beautiful roses to look at and smell and cheer her up a bit.

She'd run all the way there, and if he wasn't still around she'd ring him and explain about Frank, and not wanting to leave him to spend his last moments on earth alone. "They look as though they've come from someone's garden. And the thorns have been cut off."

"Well, go and admire them some place else, Han," Phil said. "Didn't you say you were late for a lunch date? If whoever you're meeting hasn't thought to bring you roses – and in my humble opinion he's not worth a fig if he hasn't – then at least you'll have some."

"So I will," Hannah said, clutching the roses to her. "So I will."

Adam answered on the first peep. "Adam?" she demanded.

"Yes."

"I'm phoning to apologise. I had a lunch date with you, and I know I'm more than late…"

"You're not late, Hannah," Adam said. "We can call it re-scheduled if you like."

Hannah laughed, and again Adam experienced that bone-melting feeling at the sound of it.

"I can explain. When I get there – I've not mastered walking and talking into my new phone yet. If you're still there, that is."

"I can be," Adam said. "I'm only about five minutes away." Well, he was if he sprinted and there wasn't much traffic for him to dodge on Gandy Street. "If you're there before me, just hang on. How will I recognise you?" he quipped.

The image of her hazel eyes and her deep red curls and, well, just the general loveliness of her seemed to be permanently at the front of his thoughts since they'd met. And had he mentioned the freckles across her nose?

"It's me who might not recognise you," Hannah said. "I was staring at my phone a lot when we had coffee, wasn't I?"

"You were. But that was the object of the exercise."

"Anyway," Hannah said, "just so we don't miss one another, I'll be carrying a bunch of yellow… oh no, the signal's breaking …"

And then Hannah was gone. But this time, Adam saved her number. He ran like he'd never run before back to the precinct and Bailey's.

And there she was. No, she couldn't be! Hannah, holding a bunch of yellow roses. She held them in front of her, lovingly, as brides hold their flowers on their wedding day – carefully chosen for their special reason.

She was holding the very roses he'd stolen from his mother's garden and left on a bench in the precinct. How had she got them? Not from the bench he'd left them on, because when he'd gone back ten minutes after leaving them there, they'd gone. Where, he wondered, might they have been between then and now?

You don't need to know, mate. But I've got a good feeling about this one, you and Hannah. And like your mother said, flowers – even stolen roses – have got a magic of their own… (MW)

MY MAGIC MOMENT…

"Hello, Linda, can you hear me?" The sweetest words spoken by audiologist, Claire, at Queen Elizabeth Hospital, Birmingham, when my cochlear implant was switched on, and for the first time in decades I heard sound.

"Wish You Were Here"

Before the war, they had been classmates. Now Betty was a widow and everything had changed

By Beth Francis

Tony saw Betty as soon as he entered the crowded railway station. In spite of the intervening years, he recognised her at once.

The noise and bustle faded away around him as he was transported back to primary school, being reprimanded, yet again, for pulling her plaits.

"Seen a ghost?" Lillian enquired.

"That's Betty Evans over there," he told his sister.

"Betty Telford now. Married Bill. Remember him? Killed at Tobruk."

Tony sighed. So many of their former classmates hadn't come back home after the war ended.

He didn't really feel like a day trip to Barry Island, but Lillian had insisted. She

> She remembered the fun she and her siblings had on their annual trip

ILLUSTRATIONS: SHUTTERSTOCK

said the children wanted their uncle along, and that her husband, Frank would be glad of his company.

"I used to pull Betty's hair, at school," he said. "I was too shy to talk to her, and wanted to get her attention."

"She looks a bit anxious. Go over there and say hello."

Even after his years spent in the army, his sister still tried to boss him around. He went.

Betty kept her children close, afraid to let them out of her sight. She wouldn't have come, but her mother had seen the excursion advertised in the Argus.

"Take the children," she'd urged. "A day out will do you some good, too. I'll pay the fare."

Now, listening to their excited chatter, she remembered the fun she and her siblings used to have on their annual trip to the seaside: swimming, building sandcastles, fairground rides, candy floss.

She'd forgotten, too, how much she'd loved the hustle and bustle of the station. People scurrying to and fro, the acrid smell of steam from trains pulling away, heading for Paddington, or Swansea. She hadn't been on a train for years.

"The next train to arrive at Platform One will be the 9.35 for Barry Island, calling at…"

Betty held onto Pam with one hand and clutched her handbag and the beach bag with the other.

"Stay close to me, Sue," she told her elder daughter. "We need to get on quickly when the train comes, or we won't get seats."

"Can I help with your bags?"

"Tony Jones!" Betty remembered him from school. Skinny lad. Always in trouble. Played truant a lot. Used to ➔

pull her plaits. But for that cheeky grin, she wouldn't have recognised him.

"This gentleman used to tease me when we were at school," she explained to the children.

She could see his lips moving, but his reply was drowned by the noise of their train thundering into the station, brakes squealing, as it hissed to a halt. Sue, terrified by the noise, picked up her heels and fled towards the exit.

"Sue!" Betty screamed, trying to run after her, but hampered by the need to keep tight hold of Pam, and by the confusion of families pushing forward to climb aboard the train.

"I can see her. By the barriers," Tony said. "Stay there. I'll fetch her."

As the crowds thinned, she saw him talking to Sue, saw him pointing out where she was standing with Pam, saw

said, ignoring the tutting from the queue that had formed by the carriage door, and pushing through to rejoin his sister.

Betty stood at the end of the queue, shuffling forward as the carriages filled.

Tony leaned out of the window two carriages along. "I've got seats for you," he called.

"He's nice," Sue said, as they boarded the train and walked along the corridor.

Tony had put his newspaper on one seat, a bag of beach toys on another and was sitting on the third. He stood up as they approached and helped her put her bags on the luggage rack.

"I hope you have a lovely day," he said. "If you need any help, I'll be a few carriages along, sitting with my sister and her family."

Betty felt confused and flustered as he left. One minute she'd decided to go

Self-consciously she wriggled out of her clothes while Sue held up the towel

him encouraging her daughter to come back to her side.

The fear that had gripped her eased a little. She knew she was overprotective with the children, but they were all she had. She wanted to go back home now. Back to safety.

"There'll be no seats left now. We may as well go home," she said, as Tony returned with a sheepish-looking child.

"But you said we could paddle," Sue protested, outraged.

"You'd have to get on that train first," Betty said shortly.

"It was just noisy, Mam. I'm sorry."

"Are you coming, Tony?" Lillian called, as she shepherded her family aboard the train.

"I'll get on and save seats for you," he

home, the next she was on her way to the seaside. And she hadn't properly thanked Tony for his help.

The train started to move. The other children in the carriage were standing by the window, excitedly pointing out landmarks. They made space for Sue and Pam to join them. The adults laughed indulgently as the eager youngsters tried to glimpse the sea, long before they reached Barry Island.

B etty was calmer by the time the train arrived. They followed the crowds streaming towards the beach and set out their bags and towels on the firm, tide-washed sand, away from the mass of people huddling near the wall.

"There's the man who helped us at the

station," Sue said, waving enthusiastically.

Tony waved back. He was helping his brother-in-law set up deckchairs a little further along the beach. He'd already changed into his swimming trunks. Betty saw that he wasn't skinny any more, then blushed at the wayward thought.

She helped the girls into their swimsuits, before changing herself. Not easy, even under the huge bath towel she'd brought. Self-consciously she wriggled out of her clothes, while Sue held up the towel.

"Hurry up, Mam," Pam said. "I want to go in the sea."

She took them both down to the water's edge. Sue ran in and out of the water splashing and giggling, but Pam was soon bored and wanted to build a sandcastle.

"I want to stay here in the water," Sue protested.

Betty hesitated. There were a lot of children playing happily, and she would be able to watch her from where they were sitting. The sea was calm, the waves little more than ripples.

"See the number fuve on the wall?" she said. "That's behind where we left our towels. If you can't see us when you come out of the water head for that number and you'll find us."

She helped Pam with her sandcastle, then called Sue back for lunch. As soon as she'd finished eating, Sue went back into sea, while Pam trotted up and down, fetching water to fill her moat.

Betty lay back on the sand and closed her eyes, listening to the happy chatter around her, feeling her body relax in the warmth of the sun. She could hear Tony laughing as he played beach ball with his nephews.

Four years since Bill died. She'd been pregnant with Pam. In all that time she'd never looked at another man. Why was Tony Jones making her so confused?

Her peace was shattered by Pam's anguished screams.

"It stung me, Mam. That wasp stung me!"

Betty reached into her bag for calamine lotion, poured some on a ➡

She ran. There was no sign of Sue. She could see Pam sobbing, but standing exactly where she'd been left. She hurried back towards her.

"I want Sue," Pam wailed.

"She'll be back soon," Betty tried to sound reassuring. "Remember when we were paddling, I said how to find us if you got lost?"

"Look for number five on the wall," Pam said. "She might have gone back in the water, Mam."

Betty grasped her hand and ran down to the water's edge, calling as she went.

Tony had left his nephews with their parents and gone for a long swim. All morning he'd been conscious of Betty as she paddled with her children and helped build a sandcastle. He longed to go to talk to her, but all his boyhood shyness had resurfaced.

He swam strongly, rehearsing different ways of starting a conversation. He decided to say he was fetching ice creams for his family, and would she like him to fetch some for the girls.

He was coming out of the sea when he heard her calling.

He ran across. "What's wrong?"

"I've lost Sue. I closed my eyes for a few minutes and she's disappeared. Pam says she was looking for shells."

"We'll find her," Tony said. He called Frank and the boys to help search, while Lillian took Pam back to wait by the sandcastle.

Without thinking Tony took Betty's hand as they wove between deckchairs, and round children playing, casting along the shore, first one way then the other, questioning people.

"Have you seen a girl in a green swimsuit, red hat, eight years old?" Betty asked everyone, her voice becoming more shrill with every shake of the head.

clean handkerchief and held it over the swelling, cuddling Pam until her sobs subsided into whimpers.

She looked towards the seashore and felt a flicker of unease.

"Where's Sue?"

"Looking for shells to decorate my castle. Look, she's already found a lot."

Pam proudly showed off her castle, the wasp sting forgotten.

"She should have asked before wandering off looking for shells."

"We didn't want to wake you, Mam," Pam said.

The flicker of unease turned to panic.

"I wasn't asleep. I'd just closed my eyes. How long has she been gone?"

Pam shrugged.

"Don't know. Not long."

Betty had not felt such fear since she had stood clutching the telegram about Bill. The telegram that had sent her into early labour.

"What's up, love?" The woman sitting next to them had noticed her agitation.

"I can't see my daughter."

"She may be watching the Punch and Judy show."

A crowd had gathered a little further up the beach.

"Don't move," Betty told Pam. "I'm going to see if she's watching the show."

A few people thought they'd seen her. No one was sure.

They went back to Lillian who was sitting with Pam. Frank and the boys hadn't found her either.

"Time to report her missing, then," Lillian said briskly.

Tony glared at his sister. Betty was already desperate, talk of reporting Sue missing would only panic her more. The girl must be on the beach.

"Go on, love," Lillian said. "We'll look after Pam and keep searching."

Tony watched as Betty pulled her frock over her swimsuit, grabbed her shoes and half ran, half stumbled across the hot sand, pausing by the concrete ramp only to pull her shoes on, before running up into the crowds.

She was so strong. He didn't think he could cope as she did. He wanted to go

number on the wall. I was crying but a kind man found me. He gave me sweets."

The hubbub from the beach faded. Betty felt Tony's arm round her shoulders as he supported her. She moistened her lips, struggling to keep calm. Tony could feel her shaking.

"He took me to his wife, then they brought me here. They couldn't stay because their baby needed a feed."

Betty felt a rushing in her ears, a wave of nausea washed over her, then she lost consciousness.

"Mam!" Sue screamed.

"She'll be all right, Sue. She's only fainted. It's hot today."

He knelt beside Betty. She looked so vulnerable. He wanted to protect her, and her children. If she'd let him.

"Sorry about that," she whispered, as she regained consciousness. Tony helped

"Time to report her missing, then," said Lillian briskly. Tony glared at his sister

with her, but knew he should be here in case Sue came back. She didn't know Lillian and her family.

Suddenly the Tannoy crackled into life.

"Will the mother of Sue Evans, please come to the lost children's post, where her daughter is waiting for her?"

Betty gasped with relief, and leaned over the wall. Tony was running up the beach, towards her, pulling his shirt on as he ran. Together they scurried along the promenade, past the arcades, the ice-cream sellers and the cafes to the far end of the beach and the lost children's post.

Breathless and dishevelled, they found Sue playing happily with a beach ball.

"Mam! I was lost. I was looking for shells, then I couldn't see you. I forgot the

her sit up. She rested her head on his shoulder. Sue snuggled close to her.

"Understandable," he said. "You've had a dreadful fright."

"I need to get back to Pam."

She got slowly to her feet, clinging onto his arm.

They retraced their steps, Sue holding tight to her mother's hand, while Tony walked beside them.

"Safe?" people asked, as they walked across the beach.

"Safe and well," Betty replied, sinking onto the towel and hugging both girls.

Tony sat beside her.

"I'll go and check my lot are all right," Lillian said.

"I shouldn't have closed my eyes," Betty said, wringing her hands. ➤

Both girls had already pulled away from her and were engrossed, putting shells on the castle. Pam had forgotten her wasp sting and Sue seemed to have recovered from her fright, but all Betty wanted to do was to hurry them both home safely.

"Nothing any of us hasn't done," Lillian soothed. "Don't go blaming yourself. You're a great mother – anyone can see that."

"I should have been watching them," Betty said, watching Lillian go.

"She's right, you know," Tony said. "You're a great mother."

Betty turned to look at him. His eyes were kind, full of sympathy. Somehow, in all the drama, the awkwardness between them had been forgotten.

"Can I go and paddle?" Sue asked.

"I don't think so. We'll be catching the early train home."

"But I want to fill my moat with water," Pam moaned.

"And you promised we could go on the fairground," Sue said. "Gran gave us money for two rides each."

Betty looked at their eager faces. It was a pity to disappoint them.

"All right. Play for a while, then we'll go to the fair. But you must stay close to me. No wandering off."

"Can I come with you?" Tony said. "Please." He looked so like the children when they were pleading for a treat that she was tempted to ruffle his hair.

"I owe you for all those times I pulled your plaits when we were at school," he added by way of explanation.

She felt a smile tugging at her lips as she nodded.

B etty enjoyed the fairground. She took Pam on the roundabout, then helped her throw hoops until they won a goldfish in a jam jar. Tony took Sue on the carousel, then on the scenic railway,

both emerging from the roller coaster ride looking sick, but laughing.

Bit like my day, she thought. *Terrified one minute, laughing the next.*

The train was waiting at the platform, half empty. They had a carriage to themselves. Pam settled in a corner watching her goldfish.

"His name's Winston," she said.

"I've an old goldfish bowl at home you can have," Tony told her.

Sue sat looking out of the window but by the time the train rumbled through Barry Dock both children were asleep.

Tony nudged Betty's foot and smiled at her across the carriage.

"I pulled your plaits so often, I think it'll take me for ever to make it up to you," he said softly.

Betty smiled back at him. That sounded all right to her. **Ⓜ**

. . . .

MY MAGIC MOMENT...

Leaning against a rock on Mount Teide, Tenerife, as the sun set, drinking hot chocolate and watching stars begin to appear until the sky seemed full of shimmering light.

Brain Boosters

Sudoku 1   Sudoku 2

Fill in each of the blank squares with the numbers 1 to 9, so that each row, each column and each 3x3 cell contains all the numbers from 1 to 9.

		2	7			
		5	1			
9		3	8			1
	8				7	
	1	4		5	3	
5						2
	9	4	6	2		
7						5
2	5		7		1	3

		5			3
2				1		
6	5				2	7
4	3	1			8	
		2	4			
5	9	8			6	
3	4				1	5
1			3			
		6			9

Word Wheel

Turn To Page 155 For Solutions

You have ten minutes to find as many words as possible using the letters in the wheel. Each word must be three letters or more and contain the central letter. Use each letter once and no plurals, foreign words or proper nouns are allowed. There is at least one nine-letter word.

Average: 24 words
Good: 25-36 words
Excellent: 37-47 words

Bring Me Sunshine

With love and support, children can heal themselves – and maybe even show us the way…

By Susan Sarapuk

"Maisie, where are you?" Liz called out. When there was no reply, she climbed the stairs.

She found her eight-year old niece in the bedroom, sitting on the floor in a sun spot, staring out of the window.

"There you are," she said kindly. "Didn't you hear me calling?"

"I was looking at the sky, Auntie Liz." The little girl didn't look up but continued to stare out of the window.

"What's so interesting about it?" Liz sat down at Maisie's side and crossed her legs. The sunny spot was incredibly warm.

"It's so blue, Auntie Liz. It looks like the sea, like I could swim away in it to a magic place. Maybe I'd find Mummy there."

Liz choked. Her sister had died nine months ago. Maisie had coped pretty well with the loss of her mother, but there were still times like this when she'd drift away, lost in her own world.

"I bet you could," she said.

If only it were that easy. She and Clare had been close, chatting every day on the phone if they didn't see each other, and the loss was still raw. Sometimes she'd pick up the phone to ring her sister, only to realise as she started to dial that Clare was gone. It wasn't fair that someone with a husband and child should have to die so young.

"Promise me you'll be there for Maisie," Clare had said towards the end.

"Of course I'll be there. I'm her aunt."

"And Lee – he'll struggle to get over this. Keep an eye on him for me."

She'd kept her word. Whenever she could, she looked after Maisie, taking her out for treats and excursions, trying to be everything to her niece except a mother because no one could replace her mother.

She picked up the slack when Lee couldn't be there because of late meetings at work or business trips away.

She sighed now.

"I know, Auntie Liz," Maisie said. She sighed emphatically too. "Daddy says when you haven't got words, you just let out a long sigh and Mummy knows exactly what you want to say."

"That's very good," Liz said. They sat in silence for a while before she asked, "Do you want to go out for ice cream? That's why I was calling you."

"Yes please!" Maisie jumped up.

It was remarkable how quickly an eight-year old could forget sad contemplation when ice cream beckoned.

Liz had arranged to meet Ryan that evening. He'd offered to pick her up but she'd declined. She liked the freedom of being able to make her own way; it meant that she wouldn't be able to drink too ➜

much and that she was in control, that there'd be no assumptions about what was going to happen afterwards.

She'd started seeing Ryan a couple of months before Clare's death.

"Is this going to be the one?" Her sister had teased. "You've kissed enough frogs."

"I have to make sure. I'm a bit of a slow burner. Not everyone can be as fortunate as you, falling in love instantly and never having to question it."

Ryan was waiting for her at the waterfront restaurant. He rose to greet her with a kiss.

"Sorry, am I late?" Liz apologised.

"No more than usual." He smiled. "I've ordered your drink."

Liz took off her coat, sat down and looked at the menu.

"Did you have Maisie?" Ryan asked.

"Yes. We went out for ice cream and then fed the ducks in the park."

"How is she?"

"She's a resilient little thing. I think she's

each other – I mean, I really like you."

Liz didn't reciprocate. It's not that she didn't feel the same way – she just found it hard to say it.

"Anyway, how do you feel about going to Rome for a weekend?"

She'd always wanted to go to Rome.

"I've booked separate rooms so you don't have to worry."

He was a real gentleman. Clare had said right from the start that she had the feeling that Ryan was a good one. Yet still...

"Can I see how Maisie and Lee are fixed first?" she said.

"I knew you'd say that." He grinned. "Of course, I don't want to push you."

Afterwards they strolled hand in hand along the waterfront. She wanted to believe that everything would work out with Ryan, but how could there be security in this life when a young woman in her prime could be snatched away just like that?

Maisie had to be her focus for now – she owed it to her sister.

"You can't depend on anything any more, can you? Nothing is as we expected"

teaching me to cope with bereavement rather than the other way around."

"You're good with her."

"She's my niece and I love her to bits."

"You'll be great with your own kids."

"I think Maisie's enough for now."

"I bet she'd love some cousins."

"One day." Liz shrugged. This subject had taken a rather intimate turn. Was he thinking he might be a part of it?

The meal arrived. They caught up on each other's days, then Ryan put down his knife and fork.

"This looks serious," Liz said.

"Liz, we've known each other for almost a year," he said. "Enough to know we like

The call came just after lunch.

"Is that Liz Lewis? Hello, I'm Caroline, the Head at Maisie's school. Could you come and pick her up? She's very distressed. We've taken her into a quiet room but I think she needs to go home."

There was no one else who could do it. Lee was on a business trip and Liz was named as next of kin in his absence. The only way she could get away from work was to ask for a half day's leave, but that didn't matter; she had to get to Maisie.

As soon as she was shown into the staff room Maisie ran into her arms.

"What is it, darling?" Liz hugged her.

"I want Mummy," Maisie sobbed.

"I know, I know you do." Liz caressed her hair. "Come on, let's go."

The first thing Liz did was take Maisie for ice cream. Her niece continued crying for a while, but then the pleasure of eating her treat took over. Liz was amazed at how a child could live in the moment, could let all the pain out without embarrassment, then move on to the next thing.

Afterwards they went for a walk in the park, Maisie clinging to her hand. They fed the ducks, then sat down under a tree and watched the sunlight glinting off the water.

"I miss Mummy," Maisie said.

"I do too. She was my little sister. She's looking down on us, though." Liz looked up at the sky. "What shall we say to her?"

"Hello, Mummy." Maisie waved.

"Hello, Clare."

"You look like Mummy, Auntie Liz." Maisie snuggled up to her and Liz put an arm around her shoulders.

Maisie suddenly let out a long sigh.

"Mummy knows what I want to say."

Liz sighed too. Sometimes there were no words, only sighs and hugs.

Liz pondered what to do about the trip to Rome. She spoke to Lee.

"What's your schedule for the weekend of the nineteenth next month?" she said over coffee, in the lovely new kitchen that Clare had planned and had had fitted not long before her death. "Are you away?"

"All my weekends are free next month," he said. "Have you got plans?"

"Ryan's booked a trip to Rome for us. I don't know whether I should go. It seems like a big commitment, a next step, and I'm not sure I'm ready for it."

"It sounds great – you should go. Ryan's a really great guy."

"Maisie might need me."

"I think she needs to spend time with her dad when I'm not away."

"Yeah – you're right."

"What's up, Liz? Why are you afraid?"

"Do you have to ask?"

They exchanged a knowing glance, then Lee peered into his mug.

"You can't depend on anything any more, can you?" Liz said softly. "Nothing is as we expected."

"I thought you liked Ryan." Lee looked up. "Clare does, did…"

"She thought he was a good one." It was Liz's turn to peer into her mug. "I want to be here for Maisie, for her to be my focus."

"But you can't put your life on hold," Lee reasoned. "Liz, I appreciate all you're doing for Maisie. These past few months I, we, would have been lost without you – but she has her dad."

"Yes." Liz looked up and smiled. "And that's who she needs more than anyone else, I know." ➤

"Apart from her mother…"

Lee let out a long sigh, and Liz joined him. Once again, there were no words.

Ryan hadn't pressed her for a decision on Rome. She appreciated that, but she knew she'd have to give him an answer soon, and on that answer hung the direction of their relationship. He'd been patient and understanding during her bereavement, but that couldn't last forever.

She was already scared of losing him, but if she made a commitment, then she would have even more to lose. Nothing lasted forever.

It was almost as if he knew what she was thinking.

"Nothing's a hundred per cent certain," he said as they strolled hand in hand along the waterfront, enjoying the balmy evening air. "I know, as far as I can, that I really want to be with you. I bet Lee doesn't regret any of his time with your sister, he'd take those years and his daughter even after all that's happened."

"It's just not fair." Liz sighed.

"No, it's not."

"You know, Clare really liked you." Liz stopped walking.

"She was a very intelligent woman." He squeezed her hand.

Now would have been the moment to say yes, she was going to Rome, but Liz couldn't; something was stopping her. She looked away and continued walking.

She had Maisie for the day again. They sat at Liz's kitchen table strewn paper and pencils and felt tip pens. Liz was teaching her niece how to cut out a paper mannequin, then draw and cut out clothes with tabs to attach to her.

Maisie sang as she coloured in.

"You're happy today," Liz commented.

"Yes, Auntie Liz." Maisie smiled at her and resumed her singing.

Maisie was happy, her mind emptied of sad thoughts, totally engrossed in the moment. Children had the ability to do that. Why couldn't she do it? Why wasn't she allowing herself to be happy?

Sometimes she felt it would be disloyal to Clare… but Clare would have been annoyed to see her thinking like that.

Maisie stopped singing as she concentrated on cutting out the purple and yellow dress she'd designed. Then she put down the scissors, cupped her chin in her hand and let out a long sigh.

"Are you thinking of Mummy?" Liz said.

"I'm talking to her."

Liz joined in the sigh.

Then Maisie brightened up, picked up the scissors again and continued singing.

"Have you stopped thinking of Mummy now?" Liz said.

"Oh no, Mummy's always there," Maisie said cheerfully, "but now I'm cutting out and singing." And she carried on.

Something inside Liz felt released. It was as if Clare was speaking to her. *Go ahead and live your life,* she seemed to say. *Take my daughter as an example.*

It was suddenly clear to Liz that she needed to say yes to Ryan. Whatever happened, she couldn't live in the past or use Maisie as an excuse to escape the future. She owed it to her sister to live.

She looked towards the kitchen window to see the blue sky beyond and let out another sigh – but it sounded different to all the others this time.

"I know, Auntie Liz," Maisie answered with a smile. "I know." (MW)

....

MY MAGIC MOMENT…

A trip to the Kennedy Space Centre where I saw the launch pads for the Apollo missions and the space shuttle. I always dreamed of seeing a shuttle launch but never did.

Most Magical Sporting Moments

✦ Bobby Moore holding the 1966 World Cup aloft after England's win is seen by many as an iconic sporting image.

✦ George Best was a footballing icon – not least after his six-goal scoring spree against Northampton in the 1970 FA Cup.

✦ Young Scot, David WIlkie, destroyed the field and the world record in the 200m breast stroke in the 1976 Olympics.

✦ In the 1976 Olympics, 14-year-old Olga Korbut of the Soviet Union scored a perfect 10. In fact, it showed on the score boards as 1.00 because they were not equipped for such perfection!

✦ The end of Torvill and Dean's performance at the 1984 Winter Olympics was a pure gold moment – and it was watched by 24.5 million, making it the BBC's biggest audience for a live sports event.

✦ David Beckham was epic as he scored from his own half against Wimbledon at Selhurst Park in 1996.

Jack Nicklaus made the perfect gesture and conceded the final putt to Tony Jacklin at the end of the 1969 Ryder Cup

✦ Dennis Taylor's black ball finish in the 1985 World Snooker final showcased his perfect control of temperament in order to scrape home against Steve Davis.

✦ In Ascot in 1996, Frankie Dettori was man and beast in perfect harmony as they romped home in all 7 races.

✦ Boris Becker, at the age of 17 in 1985, was not only the youngest men's Wimbledon champion, but the tournament's first unseeded winner.

✦ America's Michael Phelps gave a supreme performance at the 2007 World Swimming Championships, winning eight gold medals and setting four world records.

Getting To Know You!

This nice, relaxing day at the zoo was quickly getting out of hand for arachnophobic Auntie Sarah…

By Carrie Hewlett

"And I'm looking forward to seeing the spiders," Amber finished. Up to that point Sarah had been looking forward to spending the day at the zoo with her seven-year-old niece. As it was half term, and her sister wasn't well, her offer had been gratefully accepted.

"What?" she demanded now.

"The spiders and insects in Bug World. I mean, I love the idea of seeing all the animals but there's something so cool about spiders, don't you think?"

Sarah's face paled. She was scared stiff of spiders. How was she going to cope?

Unfortunately for her, Amber picked up a map, and kept an eager eye open.

"I've been looking forward to seeing them all day," she said.

Her young face was full of eager anticipation as they approached Bug World. No way could she disappoint her.

Sarah made some noncommittal response, feeling an overwhelming sense of dread drag her stomach to rock bottom.

Entering the dusky forest, their eyes took a few moments to adjust from the bright sunlight outside.

"Ooh, look, stick insects," Amber squealed, her nose pressed against the glass. Sarah was just thankful that there

Maybe she could avoid the spider section by pretending they were out of time?

She'd assumed they'd be seeing the normal sort of animals you might see at the zoo. The cute and cuddly ones, maximum four legs. Bringing spiders into the equation was another matter entirely.

"I'm looking forward to seeing the tigers," she said, changing the subject.

Amber agreed and Sarah breathed a sigh of relief. Maybe she could just avoid the spider section by pretending they were running out of time or something?

was glass. She'd never been a fan of creepy crawlies even as a child, and could still recall vividly the terror she had felt when her brother had placed a plastic spider in her bed.

"This is *so* amazing," Amber enthused.

Sarah grinned, loving to see her niece's young face lighting up as bright as the sunlight they'd just left behind when they'd entered the darkened building. Hopefully this wouldn't be for long. She'd just have to grin and bear it until they got back outside.

Rounding the bend, having meandered through the marine world and past some very colourful beetles, they reached the spider section. Sarah tried her best to smile and look interested – even though she longed to race past.

Up ahead she noticed that there seemed to be some sort of gathering.

Amber jostled through to the front – ever anxious to be at the centre of whatever was going on – and Sarah feeling duty-bound to follow.

"So, if you fancy the idea of actually holding a spider, or conquering a fear, the last session for today is due to start in a few minutes," a woman was saying.

"Ooh! Can we? Pleeeease?" Amber spun round and looked up at her aunt with beseeching eyes.

Gulping, and unable to think of a suitable reason as to why not, Sarah found herself following Amber into a small room off the main corridor.

Glancing around, she counted about twelve people in total, including two other children and a small gaggle of teenagers.

She looked at Amber, who was gazing in wonder at two ominous Perspex boxes sitting at one end of the room.

"This is brilliant!" she squeaked.

"Isn't it," Sarah replied with a shudder.

"I don't think you really mean that, do you?" a voice at her side whispered.

It was the most delicious-sounding voice she'd ever heard. Like dark brown velvet, or liquid chocolate.

Turning, she came face to face with a man about her own age, in his late twenties, with twinkling brown eyes.

"How can you tell?" she murmured. →

"I'm an expert." The man winked.

Sarah was about to respond when the room was silenced by the same woman who'd enticed them in earlier.

"Hi everyone. I'm so pleased that we've got so many people interested in getting up close and personal to these specimens of Araneae. To tell you more, and lead you through this, can I introduce you to Adam. He's an expert and a real spider enthusiast."

The man beside Sarah stepped forward, with a broad grin.

Sarah's mouth twitched. He'd been telling the truth when he'd said he was an expert. Was it her imagination or did his gaze rest slightly longer on herself?

Slightly self-conscious, she pushed a strand of her dark hair behind one ear, feeling a blush spread across her cheeks.

She took in his casual jeans and long-sleeved shirt, watching as he brushed a hand through dark brown wavy hair, feeling her heart thud. Strange. She hadn't felt this immediate attraction towards someone for quite a while.

Amber brought her attention back to the present by whispering, "What happens next, Auntie?"

Sarah shrugged, bringing a finger to her mouth to shush her.

Adam proceeded to give a short talk about the arachnids. The way he spoke with such ardour invoked even Sarah's interest. Her gaze locked onto his animated features as he spoke with

passion about… what she considered to be something repugnant.

With his deep, sexy voice he could make anything sound heavenly, she decided, her pulse fluttering at the way his eyes crinkled delightfully at the corners.

"Do you think they'll let us hold a spider?" Amber asked in a loud whisper.

Sarah swallowed hard. "I wouldn't have thought so," she whispered back.

"Tarantulas are night-time hunters which will pounce on their prey. There are around seven hundred different kinds in the world and they eat insects, beetles and grasshoppers." Adam paused. "Now, who'd like to take a closer look at them?"

Amber's hand shot up and Sarah's heart plummeted.

Adam beckoned her closer, giving Sarah a perceptive look.

"Why don't you come up too?"

Sarah shook her head, but Amber pulled on her hand.

"Come on, Auntie."

Warily Sarah followed her niece, inching forward with hesitant steps.

The first box held a small, greyish spider intricately spinning its web. *Bearable to look at, maybe,* she thought grimly. Her gaze then flicked to the bigger tank and she drew a sharp breath seeing a large tarantula.

"Oh, this is *so* cool," Amber said with a look of awe.

"Way cool," Sarah said faintly.

Her gaze caught Adam's and she saw him give her an amused look.

Glancing away, Sarah focussed on the teenagers who were pointing and giggling, egging each other on.

She looked back at Adam who gave a smile of encouragement.

"Just look at Pete. Such a beautiful rose-pink colour. This breed can range from light grey to a vibrant pink. He can't escape, so don't worry. Walk around the tank if you like, and have a good look at him, he won't mind."

Sarah shuddered.

Concentrating on Amber, she watched as her niece gazed in awe at the arachnid.

"Do you think Mum will let me have one as a pet?"

"Umm. Shouldn't think so!"

Amber made a face.

"I might still ask for one for my birthday. I mean, you never know."

"They do make fun pets for some people," Adam said. "Very docile, with low maintenance." Sarah detected a definite smiley tone to his voice. "But you do have to be careful with them."

"So maybe not suitable for someone as young as Amber," Sarah interjected, with

"He's really cute, honest," Amber said.

"He's probably had enough stroking for now," Adam said, saving her. Sarah breathed a sigh of relief when Amber decided not to push it, giving Adam another grateful look.

"OK. Now if you'd all like to take a step back, so as to not crowd him," Adam said, lifting Pete out carefully with a strong capable hand. "Who feels they'd like to hold him?"

"Me! Me!" Amber cried.

Sarah's gaze met Adam's once more and she shrugged helplessly.

"She likes spiders," she said weakly.

Very gently Adam placed the pink-tinted Chilean rose tarantula into Amber's small hands.

Amber's eyes widened in surprise as her fingers stroked the quivering spider

a raised eyebrow. Her face left him in no doubt as to what sort of response she hoped he would give.

"Maybe better to think about when you're a bit older," Adam said, getting the hint, before raising his voice to address the room. "Would anyone like to put their hand inside and touch him?"

Amber's face lit up as bright as a newly stamped coin and Sarah grimaced. She caught Adam's gaze once more and he grinned reassuringly at her.

"You don't have to," he mouthed.

She gave a faint, grateful grin in return, before gazing with fondness at Amber whose eyes were widening in surprise as her fingers stroked the quivering spider. "He's so soft and furry," she exclaimed.

"Nice, isn't he?" Adam said.

Amber nodded. "Come on, Auntie. You've got to have a go."

"No, no, I'm fine…" Sarah started.

Sarah wasn't completely sure what happened next. One moment Amber was holding Pete, the next her hands opened and Pete fell to the floor before bolting in a bid for freedom.

"He just slipped," Amber wailed.

Amid the ensuing screams and commotion, Sarah grabbed Amber's hands. "Are you OK?" she demanded, afraid that the tarantula had bitten her.

"I'm fine. Where is he?" Amber said tearfully, her gaze sweeping the room.

Thankful that Amber wasn't hurt, Sarah turned her attention to the chaos around them. Seeing Adam chasing Pete into a corner, and acting on instinct, she grabbed the empty Perspex container. ➡

Running after them, she brought it firmly down over Pete, trapping him.

"Thanks," Adam said, looking up to see who'd helped. Realising it was her, he grinned. "Just shows how fast they can travel, huh?"

"I am so sorry," Sarah said, feeling like she should apologise for Amber.

"Is he OK?" Amber asked with a worried face. "I didn't hurt him, did I? I really didn't mean to drop him. He just sort of slipped."

Adam didn't seem at all alarmed.

"He's fine. Don't worry. You're not the first and won't be the last to do that. And well done to your auntie for grabbing the container. I normally grab it myself just in case."

Lifting Pete and the container, Adam returned them to the table.

Seeing Amber still looking distressed, Sarah put an arm around her shoulders.

"It's OK, sweetie. All sorted. Maybe leave asking your mum for a spider as a pet for a bit, though, huh," she said, trying to lighten the situation.

Amber nodded. "Yeah, I'll wait until my hands are a bit bigger."

"Everything's OK. Alarm over. Thanks, everyone. If you'd like to head out, you'll see plenty more attractions before you exit the wonderful world of insects and bugs," the woman announced, ushering everyone towards the door.

As they left, Sarah breathed a sigh of relief. "Let's head over to the picnic area for something to drink," she said.

Quickly glancing back, she searched for Adam. Unfortunately, he seemed to have disappeared and she felt a stab of disappointment.

Having purchased a juice for Amber and a welcome cuppa for herself, they wandered closer towards the playground, where they found a seat.

"Can I join you?" said a deep, distinctive voice.

Looking up Sarah saw Adam.

"I'm glad I found you. I got waylaid. Thank goodness I overheard you say you were heading in this direction, else I might have had to put a message out over the loud-speaker system." He grinned.

"Did we forget something?"

"Well, I was kind of hoping that maybe you'd let me have your number?" Sarah saw a look of hope on his face. "Maybe we could meet up for a drink?"

She grinned, feeling her heart leap.

"I'd like that."

"You've got a way cool job," Amber announced, having guzzled her drink already. "Can I go over to the playground now, Auntie Sarah?"

"As long as you don't go far and I can keep an eye on you," Sarah said. Looking at Adam, she joked, "I think she wants a job here when she's older."

"I'm sure she'll fit right in." Adam gave a warm smile. "She's got just the right kind of personality."

Sarah smiled back, liking the spider expert more and more.

Leaving the zoo later, she could feel a warm glow of excitement flooding her being. She laughed as Amber skipped beside her, chattering away.

Unlike Amber, she wasn't sure she'd ever want to actually get close to spiders. But getting close to a spider expert – well, that was an entirely different matter and one that she looked forward to experiencing. Ⓜ

....

MY MAGIC MOMENT...

Winning my car in a newspaper-run competition! When the key I chose opened the door, the siren went off and the balloons popped – I was totally shocked but oh, so thrilled!

Celebration Time

Helping Hand Shorties

Ingredients (Makes 16)

- ◆ **180g butter, softened**
- ◆ **100g caster sugar**
- ◆ **1tsp vanilla extract**
- ◆ **315g plain flour**
- ◆ **75g ready to roll red icing**

1 Line 2 large baking trays with baking parchment. Beat butter and sugar together until soft and creamy. Stir in the vanilla.

2 Sift the flour on top, mix well and then bring together with your hands to form a firm dough. Turn on to a lightly floured surface and knead gently until smooth.

3 Roll out the mixture to a thickness of ½cm and cut out hands using an 8.5 x 7.5cm hand cutter. Re-roll the trimmings to make 16 hands. Transfer to the baking trays and chill for 30min.

4 10min before baking, preheat the oven to 180°C, Fan Oven 160°C, Gas Mark 4. Bake for about 20min until lightly golden. Cool for 10min then transfer to a wire rack to cool completely.

5 Roll out the red icing thinly and cut out 3.5cm wide hearts. Stick on to the shorties using a little water. Leave to dry for 1-2hr before packing. → P 137

RECIPE AND FOOD STYLING: KATHRYN HAWKINS PHOTOGRAPHY: STUART MACGREGOR

Smiles And Sunflowers

The wildness of her late mother's long-abandoned allotment holds poignant and precious memories...

By Janette Sykes

O K, so where do we start?" I know without looking at Dad that he's just as clueless as I am.

"Dunno, love." The crack in his voice tugs at my heart. "The allotment was your mum's baby. She loved this place."

"Looks like this baby's outgrown her bootees," I say as I reach for his warm, comforting hand as I scan the grossly overgrown plot.

It's a riot of late summer flowers, vegetables and fruit. Runner beans curl round canes, pods bursting, long gone to seed. Caterpillar-ravaged cabbages spread large leaves like dark green lace.

Raspberries rot on a forest of canes, looking blood red in the bright sunshine.

And the weeds! Nature has slowly been reclaiming her territory, and grass, feathery with ripening seeds, has grown waist-high, threaded through with a profusion of wildflowers. Dandelions and buttercups are having a field day.

"Your mum liked it to be a bit wild." It's as if Dad is reading my thoughts.

I squeeze his hand. "Even she would have drawn the line at this," I say, suddenly wistful. "The only thing I ever won a prize for at primary school was for growing the tallest sunflower, and it was Mum's magic that saw to that. I had nothing to do with it."

This time Dad squeezes my hand as I fight back tears. "She always said they reminded her of smiling faces," he recalls. "My only contribution was to build her that bird table – do you remember it?"

"Yes, it was great – it looked like a tree house, with a proper lead covered roof to keep out the rain. You put some hooks on it so she could hang feeders on it…"

With a pang, I remember I promised Mum I would come down and feed the birds, a promise I failed to keep.

"She always made sure the feeders were topped up, and she used to slip the blackbirds a handful of raisins each day. She thought it stopped them eating her raspberries, but looking at them I'm not so sure," says Dad.

We both manage a smile. Since Mum lost her fight for life in the spring, it's taken us both months to face coming down to the allotment. The last thing she did was to plant her runner beans at the end of May. And she told me to come down and pick them. Another promise I didn't keep.

Neither Dad nor I have been able to face it until now. There's been so much to do, so much grief to work through, that we haven't had the energy. Faced with this exuberant explosion of life, I now realise why. It's almost as if, by letting the allotment simply be, we've been able to pretend that Mum is still here, tending her beans and cabbages, picking her raspberries, then lounging in her deckchair with a cup of tea, listening to her beloved birdsong.

Now I can understand why, in the face of her mortality, Mum wanted to create life, a continuing legacy to share with us, something vibrant and flourishing to remember her by… I even understand why she insisted on planting seeds that she would never harvest, and seeing blossom that would mature into fruit she would never pick.

I feel a sharp stab of guilt that we have taken so long to confront reality, though I like to think she would understand. We've been through so many emotions over the last few months, and there is so much more healing to be done. So here we are, finally, in the place that she loved best.

Faced with the tangible and inescapable evidence that she is no ➡

longer with us, we both know it's time to tidy the place up. Neither of us know what we're doing, but we owe it to Mum's memory to somehow find the strength to give it a go.

Silently, we set to.

Dad unravels the runner beans while I uproot the remains of the cabbages. We both haul out huge tussocks of grass and tufts of buttercups and dandelions, creating a messy delving into his backpack and fishing out a flask and two mugs. There's much more work to be done, but there will be other days to do it. I don't think Dad or I will ever be experts, but we'll give it our best shot.

I leave Dad to it and weave carefully through the fruit trees in search of his bird table at the far end of the allotment. Carefully I part the branches of the last

Neither Dad nor I know what we're doing, but we owe it to Mum's memory

mountain of plants and roots.

As we work, it dawns on me why Mum loved gardening so much. I come to appreciate the physical connection with the plants and the soil, the smell of freshly turned earth, the feeling of being a part of the cycle of life. And the birdsong, of course. I feel a great wave of peace and satisfaction wash over me. I'm even thinking I might take on the allotment next year.

By the time Dad is cutting back the raspberry canes, several hours have slid by and, backs aching, we have finally cleared a path through to the fruit trees. Their branches are burgeoning with fast-swelling apples and pears and even I realise they'll soon be ready for picking.

Memories of Mum's home made pies, jams and puddings flood my mind, and I make a mental promise to get baking when they're ripe – determined that this is a pledge I will definitely keep.

"Time for tea, I reckon," says Dad,

tree and step through. My heart leaps.

There it is, next to Mum's weather-beaten shed and her striped deckchair, looking a bit battered and strung with long-empty bird feeders, though the lead-covered roof is still going strong.

Surrounding it is a swathe of exquisite sunflowers, as tall as the tree house, their upturned faces beaming at the sky.

Dad taps me tenderly on the shoulder. I turn, and we wrap our arms around each other, hugging as tight as we can.

"Wild is wonderful," I say. "But sunflowers really are the best." 🅜

• •

MY MAGIC MOMENT...

The day I learned I had won tickets to see the Sleeping Beauty Ice Show in London, as a prize in the national TV Comic Essay Competition. It was the early 1960s, I was seven and it was just before Christmas – the best present ever!

Brain Boosters

Kriss Kross

Try to fit all the listed words back into the grid.

Turn To Page 155 For Solutions

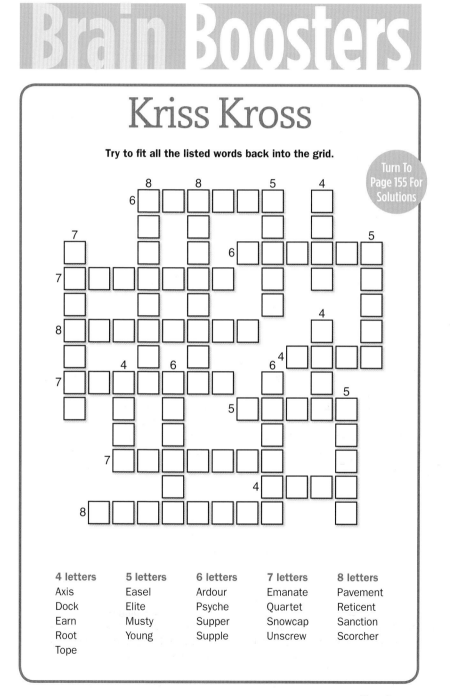

4 letters	5 letters	6 letters	7 letters	8 letters
Axis	Easel	Ardour	Emanate	Pavement
Dock	Elite	Psyche	Quartet	Reticent
Earn	Musty	Supper	Snowcap	Sanction
Root	Young	Supple	Unscrew	Scorcher
Tope				

Sunset Summer

He came from a different world yet in those golden days, he became my brother

By Lynda Franklin

Frank was a funny lad. Skinny as you like and so short-sighted he would peer through his National Health glasses until it seemed he was looking straight through you.

He arrived in a proper pair of trousers and long-sleeved shirt, with a hand-knitted bottle green jumper slipped over the top. Smart, really. Certainly smarter than the kids round here looked most of the time. He held out his hand in greeting and our Joanie giggled uncontrollably until

Mother glared at her. We all shook hands. I'd never shaken hands with anyone before and it felt really strange, a real grown-up thing to do.

"Come on then, let's get you home." Mother had picked up his case and led us out of the village hall. There were people everywhere – some we knew well, and a lot I'd never seen before.

"Will we be going by bus or taxi?" Frank asked, peering up at her through his thick lenses.

Mother pursed up her mouth a bit.

"We'll be walking. That's what we do

round here, we walk. You'll wait all day if you wait for a bus. It'll only take half an hour or so, but we'd better get a move on. I've left a nice bit of mutton in the oven and I don't want it to burn."

Her face softened then, as if suddenly realising how difficult this might be for him.

"I did some baking earlier – got a nice batch of jam tarts waiting for you. Would you like one with a glass of warm milk when we get back?"

Frank nodded and Joanie, being Joanie, grabbed hold of his hand. "Let's run!" she said, pulling at his arm.

"No, we'll walk thank you, Joanie," Mother said firmly.

And so we did. The four of us. And by the time we reached our terraced cottage, I'd decided this new boy would be the brother I'd always wanted. There was no reason why I couldn't pretend anyway, for as long as he was with us.

Frank looked around our cottage taking everything in. He told us it was smaller than his house but a lot nicer.

"Why's that, then?" Joanie asked him. "Do you live in a slum? Everyone lives in slums in London, don't they?" ➡

"Of course they don't!" Mother said. "I'm sure Frank's got a very nice house. He's only here because of the bombs – I told you that. They get a lot of bombs going off in London. He's come to the country to keep safe."

"Why's he come on his own? Didn't your mum and dad want to come?"

Mother went to reply, her mouth all tight looking again, but Frank pushed his spectacles to the back of his nose and said, "My father's on a ship I think, and my mother has to look after the shop."

"I'd hate it if I had to go away." It was hard to stop Joanie once she started. I felt sorry for Frank. He must feel so strange in this house, in the middle of the country, with a family he'd never met before. I

"I'm not sure how long I'm here for."

"You can stay forever if you like."

Frank looked uncertain then, but I really wanted a brother.

"Maybe." he said.

Joanie and I taught Frank to catch the tiny fish that swam in the ponds, and to let them go without hurting them. We made dens from sticks and twigs and played hide and seek among the bushes and trees. I showed him how to collect eggs from Dora our hen and Joanie helped him make daisy chain crowns for his head.

The summer sky was blue and the days hot and sunny. Warm evenings were lit by brilliant red and orange sunsets, and Frank, Joanie and I would sit on the front garden wall and watch the big red sun

We made dens from sticks and twigs, and I showed him how to collect eggs

smiled at him and he smiled back.

"Come and see my bedroom," I said. "I've got some boy books and a boy puzzle if you want them."

Mother gave me a grateful look as I took him up the narrow staircase.

We were used to the rolling hills and scratchy grassed meadows, but Frank said his home was full of bricks and funny smells and he played in the road.

I watched him, the first time we took him out to play. He stood at the top of the hill, closed his eyes against the glare of the sun, and inhaled lots of big exaggerated breaths.

"Fresh air feels different," he told me.

"Does it?"

"Oh yes. Very different. I need to breathe it in deep, so it stays with me when I go home."

"You can breathe it in every day if you like. Then it will last."

until it finally disappeared from view. Then we would run back to the cottage and play cards together, or maybe snakes and ladders.

Sometimes Mother would join in. Sometimes she would say she was too tired and fall asleep in the chair. If that happened, she would always wake up grumpy and tell us it was late and we should be in bed. Then we'd all run up the stairs and talk quietly to each other in our beds until one by one we became sleepy.

Joanie always went to sleep first, then Frank and I would chat. He would tell me about London and his life at home, and it all seemed so much more interesting than my life.

"I'll come and visit you in London one day," I told him.

Frank nodded seriously. He didn't look so much like Frank now, dressed in old shorts and top, his hair a bit too long. He wasn't so skinny either, filling out on Mother's puddings and mugs of cocoa she insisted we drink. He adjusted his glasses, and I could see his pointed little face was filling out too.

"I think the country air agrees with you." I said. I heard Mother say that once to someone and it sounded very grown-up.

"Yes, I think it does. I've breathed such a lot of it in now."

"That's good." I yawned then. "Shall I sing you a lullaby Frank?"

Frank snuggled under his covers and I sang *Rock-a-bye-baby* three times, stroking his head softly, watching his eyes flutter until they closed and didn't re-open. Then I climbed into bed and went to sleep.

One day Frank got a letter and he sat at the kitchen table and cried. I cried with him, even though I didn't know what was in the letter, and Joanie held his hand.

Mother gave him a glass of milk and told him the war would soon be over.

"You'll be home before you know it," she said. "Would you like to write a letter back to your mother?"

I found him some paper and two pencils and sat beside him as he tried to think what to write.

"Are you sad, then?" I asked. I didn't want him to miss his home. He was part of my family now. He was my brother.

"A bit."

"Don't you like it here?"

He nodded, and wrote *Dear Mum*.

"When the war's over, you and your family can move here. Then we can see each other all the time."

It seemed a reasonable compromise.

He smiled then. "Shall I write that?"

"Better not. Just say you're well and getting lots of fresh air."

"I could tell her about Dora?"

"Yes, tell her about Dora if you like."

Frank had nice handwriting, neat and rounded, and when he wrote his tongue stuck out.

"Why are you sticking your tongue out like that?"

He shrugged. "It just happens."

"Is that what you all do in London?"

"I don't know. Maybe."

He finished the letter and Mother promised she would post it.

"Go and play now," she told us. "A bit of fresh air is all Frank needs."

We played out the whole day, not even coming back for a sandwich. We played in the meadow until the sun began to set and the blue sky merged into golden streaks. We lay on our backs then, waiting for the big red sun to appear and signal the end of the day.

"You know, we won't be so far away really." Frank said thoughtfully, chewing a blade of grass.

"Don't be daft. London's ages away."

"If you think about it –" Frank had the look on his face now that Mother said showed he was clever – "I'll look up at the moon when I'm back home, and you'll look up at the moon here, and we'll be looking at the same moon at exactly the same time."

I smiled at him.

"You're clever, you are, Frank."

He shrugged. "The moon always seems bigger here though, and the stars brighter. I can't always see the stars at home." ➡

"But you can see the moon, can't you?"

"Yes, I can see the moon."

I reached out and squeezed his hand. "That's fine, then."

Mother baked a cake the day the war ended and we all sat round the wireless listening to Mr Churchill. Mother said he'd saved us all and was a good man.

I wasn't sure I liked him, though. After all, ending the war meant that Frank would have to go home.

We waved him off from the station and Joanie made a fuss about smoke getting in her eyes.

"I don't like trains," she said.

I didn't like them either. I wished there were no trains anywhere in the whole world, then Frank wouldn't be able to leave us. I watched him climb into a carriage with other boys and girls and saw him push his way to the window. We all waved until he disappeared from sight.

I waved until the train completely disappeared, in case he could still see me. My arm hurt when I finally put it down.

We walked home in silence, apart from Joanie complaining her eyes were stinging. Mother held my hand, which she never did.

"Rations will go further now, I suppose," she murmured, as if the thought had just occurred to her.

That night I stood at my bedroom window looking up at the moon. It seemed brighter than ever, shining in the blackness above the hills we used to run and play in every day.

"Are you looking, Frank?" I whispered.

"Are you looking up at our moon?"

I stood there for a long time, not wanting to go in case Frank was still looking. In the end my eyes grew so tired I climbed into bed, leaving the curtains open. From my pillow I could see the moon, and I lay staring at it until I drifted off to sleep.

Draw the curtains, luv. You'll turn into a blooming werewolf if you stare at that moon much longer."

I laughed softly and slipped into bed next to him. "You know I always look at the moon before going to bed."

"Waste of money, having curtains."

"Stop being so grumpy, you know you don't mean it."

He chuckled. "Night, luv."

I lay on my back listening to Arthur snoring softly next to me. Next door I could hear baby Sheila snuffling in her cot. Frank hadn't met her yet, but in three days' time he would be here for another visit. And I couldn't wait.

Being grown up didn't alter the bonds and feelings set in childhood. We may now have families of our own, but once we ran through sunlit meadows and counted the stars together. Once, as the War raged somewhere far away, we dreamed of a time when people who loved each other would not have to be parted.

We were the lucky ones. In the middle of the awfulness of war, we found a special friendship and love that will bind Frank, Joanie and I forever. Frank is my brother, and always will be. **MW**

♥ Celebration Time

Ice Cream Cakes

Ingredients (Makes 16)

- **16 flat-bottomed wafer cones**
- **175g baking margarine**
- **175g caster sugar**
- **1tsp vanilla extract**
- **200g self-raising flour**
- **3 medium eggs**
- **640g vanilla frosting**
- **Hundreds and Thousands**
- **8 mini flakes, halved**

1. Preheat the oven to 180°C, Fan Oven 160°C, Gas Mark 4. Sit the cones in muffin tins to hold them upright. Put margarine, sugar, vanilla, flour and eggs in a large mixing bowl, and beat using an electric whisk until creamy and smooth.

2. Use a teaspoon, spoon the mixture into each cone to two-thirds fill them. Bake in the muffin tins for 30min until risen, golden and firm to the touch. Cool on a wire rack.

3. To decorate, spoon the frosting into a piping bag fitted with a large star nozzle, and pipe a generous swirl of icing on each. Decorate with sprinkles and mini chocolate flakes. Store in an airtight container until ready to display.

RECIPE AND FOOD STYLING: KATHRYN HAWKINS PHOTOGRAPHY: STUART MACGREGOR

One False Step

New decor, new car, and now a new floor out of the blue. What on earth was Bev's husband up to?

By Glenda Young

I don't know why you had to go and get hardwood flooring, Joe. I really liked that beige carpet we had. Why couldn't we have kept it? I only had it cleaned last month!"

Bev swung her handbag off her shoulder, threw it onto the sofa and sank down into one of its cushions. She couldn't believe what her husband had done while she'd been out at work.

When she'd left the house that morning, she never thought she'd be coming home to find the living room carpet ripped up, gone, taken out and disposed of – and in its place, a newly laid hardwood floor. They hadn't even discussed changing the floor – and where had the money come from?

"How did you manage to get it done so quickly?" she demanded of Joe. "I mean, you must have had it all planned. Carpet fitters just don't turn up on a whim. You must have rung them and arranged it weeks ago."

"It wasn't weeks ago," Joe mumbled under his breath. "It was months ago."

"Months?" Bev cried. "But why on earth didn't you tell me about it? And how much has it all cost?"

"I took the money from the joint account," he replied, shrugging. "It cost two grand, more or less."

He planned to keep quiet about the more or less part.

Bev stared at the floor.

"I don't like it, Joe."

"Looks fine to me." He sniffed.

"It's too dark for a start," Bev said. She felt tears welling behind her eyes and a lump in her throat.

It wasn't the flooring that was getting to her – she knew that – but the floor was proving to be the last straw.

Joe had been acting oddly lately. Changing their living room carpet for a hardwood floor without asking her first, without talking it over between the two of them, was just another thing he had taken on himself to change around the house.

It wasn't the flooring getting to her, but it was proving to be the last straw

That's when he'd been home, of course. Most of his time over the last few months had been spent working late at the office, or his company had been sending him away on business trips for days on end.

Bev didn't mind, they were young and in love and saving up for holidays, so she never suspected what was really going on.

And yet, before the hardwood floor was installed, Joe had stripped wallpaper off the stairs and landing and painted ➔

the walls a shade of blue that Bev hadn't been keen on. Again, he'd done it without talking it through with her, without asking for her ideas. She'd just come home from work and there they were – blue walls up and down the stairs.

And then there was their car that he'd changed for a larger model, an estate car no less. She wasn't too concerned about the car because she thought if Joe was going through a mid-life crisis then he'd have bought a sports car, a red one, not an old clapped-out brown estate. But this floor, this hardwood floor that had been installed in the hours while she had been at work – it felt like the final straw to Bev. She sat stock still on the sofa, staring at the floor, trying to take it all in.

"Here, I bought you these," Joe said. He handed Bev a white carrier bag. "I went down the market earlier. Thought you'd like them."

Bev took the bag and peered inside.

"Slippers?" she cried. "But I never wear slippers! You know that."

"Thought we'd need them on the hardwood floor," Joe said. "Bought myself a pair too."

Bev pulled two pairs of slippers from the bag. One pair was fleecy brown and the smaller pair were fleecy pink, but otherwise identical in style.

"They're actually quite nice." She gave a small laugh. "But I still wish we'd talked about getting rid of the carpet first. Promise me you won't do anything else about the house, Joe, unless we talk it through together?"

But Joe didn't answer her – he was already walking away along the hall. Bev pulled off her black work shoes and pushed her tired, aching feet into the pink slippers. They fitted well and felt soft. She stood from the sofa but as soon as she did, one foot slipped out in front of her – the slippers wouldn't grip on the hardwood floor.

She tried to balance but couldn't – her feet were slipping all over the floor as if she was a novice skater on ice. She reached down to the sofa to steady herself and took off the slippers.

She turned them over in her hand and looked at the soles, wondering if she could stick something on to make them grip better. Until then, she thought, she'd have to make do with walking around in a pair of socks on the new hardwood floor.

Meanwhile, in the kitchen, Joe's phone buzzed into life with a text message. He glanced at it quickly then slid the phone into the back pocket of his jeans.

Bev walked into the kitchen, carrying the slippers.

"Who was that on the phone?" she asked, nodding to Joe's pocket.

"No one," he replied. "Bev?"

"What?"

"I'm going out tonight. I've got that thing to go to – you know, the one I told you about. With Rob."

"You're going out again? Joe, I've hardly seen you all week, you're either at work or you're out with your mates. We never spend any time together and now this… you're changing the house bit by bit without asking me, without telling me what you're doing.

"Is there something going on, Joe?

Something I need to know about?"

Joe just shook his head, turned and headed upstairs. He got changed into a clean T-shirt and jeans before heading out of the door and driving off in the estate car that Bev didn't like.

That evening, while Joe was out, Bev tried again with the slippers. She slid her feet into them while she was in the kitchen and tried to walk on the lino on the kitchen floor.

But again, just as in the living room, her feet slipped and skidded this way and that. She steadied herself, holding on to the fridge door as if her life depended on it, and slowly pulled off one slipper then the other. She breathed a sigh of relief

earring with a red stone embedded in it.

It wasn't one of hers, she knew that much – she never bought herself gold jewellery, only silver.

Her stomach turned over as a wave of anxiety hit her hard. If the earring wasn't hers, then there could only be one explanation. Another woman had been in their bedroom – and in their bed.

She sat with the earring clenched in her hand, her mind working and wondering, jigsaw pieces falling into place, making sense, making her see the bigger picture.

How had she been so stupid not to have seen it before? Changing the carpet, painting the walls, buying a different car – none of that had been for her benefit.

No – Joe had been steadily getting his

It was then that she saw it – something glistening under the bed they shared

that she could finally stand still.

She tried again, this time putting the slippers on in her bedroom where there was carpet, but the oddest thing happened there too. Instead of being able to walk step by step across the carpet, the slippers seemed to stick. In frustration, Bev sat down on the edge of the bed and ripped the slippers off with both hands.

"Stupid cheap things," she said out loud and then threw the offending footwear to the floor.

Sighing, she stood up and then bent down to retrieve them. It was then that she saw it – something glistening under the bed she shared with Joe.

She knelt down and pushed her hand under the bed to retrieve the tiny item that had caught her eye. She grasped it in her hand and pulled it towards her.

It was an earring, just one, a tiny gold

nest ready to bring in someone new.

His distance over the last few months began to make sense. The phone calls that had come into their landline when the caller hung up each time she'd answered the phone. It all started to fall into place. Their joint account statements that had cash withdrawals that Joe couldn't, or wouldn't, explain. He'd blamed the bank and said it had been a fault in their system, but now… oh, now Bev knew she had been stupid to believe all his lies.

She threw the earring to the carpet, picked up the pink slippers and squeezed them in her fists, her fury burning inside.

When Joe returned home much later that night, he expected Bev to be in bed asleep. But she was waiting for him, on the sofa. Beside her on the floor lay the pink fleece slippers. The television was on, switched to a channel playing ➝

pop music videos from the Eighties, a programme Bev normally liked. But she wasn't watching tonight. On her knee she had the laptop open on the internet banking page for their joint account. She never usually bothered with the account, she left all that to Joe who knew all the passwords and the standing order details. Bev counted seven transfers of sums of cash to a woman called Louise, dating back as far as a year. Had it really been going on for that long?

The money I've been working my socks off for in a grubby office, day in, day out? The money you said we were saving towards a holiday this year?"

Joe put his head in his hands.

"How did you find out?" he asked, hardly daring to look at Bev.

"It doesn't matter how I found out. We need to talk this out, Joe. I won't beg you to stay with me, I won't be anyone's second choice. But we need to talk it out, decide what we're doing and when

Joe sat stock still. His mouth opened and closed, but no words came out

Bev stiffened when she heard the sound of Joe's key in the front door lock.

She folded down the lid of the laptop and slid it away onto to the table by the side of the sofa. She smiled brightly at her husband as he walked into the room.

"Thought you'd be in bed," he said.

"Thought I'd stay up and get used to looking at this floor." She smiled again.

Joe's eyes were caught by the sight of the pink slippers lying beside the sofa.

"Do they fit all right?" he asked her.

"Oh, yes, they fit fine," Bev replied. "Try yours on – go on."

Joe opened the carrier bag still lying beside the sofa and took out the brown fleece slippers. He sat on the sofa beside Bev, took off his shoes and put his feet into the slippers.

"Does Louise like slippers too?" Bev asked sweetly.

Joe sat stock still. His mouth opened and closed but no words came out.

"And does Louise like blue walls and an old brown estate car?" Bev continued. "And does Louise like the money you've been giving her from our joint account?

you're moving out."

"No," Joe began. "No… I'm not moving anywhere. If we split up, then you go. I need the house for…"

"…your fancy woman?"

Joe glared at his wife.

"And the baby, when it comes."

"I need a brandy," Bev said. "There's some in the kitchen. Go and bring it in, Joe, with a couple of glasses. Looks like it's going to be a long night."

Joe stood up from the sofa, wearing his new slippers. He took a step forward and his feet slipped on the floor, his legs unable to hold him.

He reached out to Bev for balance, for help, appealing to her to support him, stop him falling and smashing his head on the hardwood floor.

But Bev just smiled, reached out and gave him a little push. Ⓜ

MY MAGIC MOMENT…

A summer day when I was 53, when not only was my first novel Belle Of The Back Streets **accepted by an agent but I had three publishers fighting for it!**

Most Memorable Royal Trivia

✦ The Royal Family refer to Buckingham Palace simply as "The House".

✦ The Queen is the 40th British monarch since William the Conqueror obtained the crown of England.

✦ It's reported that Kate and William are not allowed to bring their black cocker spaniel Lupo to the Queen's Sandringham residence for fear he'll get into a scrap with her beloved corgis.

✦ The Queen uses her handbag to signal to her ladies-in-waiting; moving it from arm to arm means she's tired of speaking to someone, and putting it on the dinner table means she's ready to leave.

✦ King Edward VIII abdicated in 1936 in order to marry the American divorcee, Wallis Simpson. Happily, today's Royals needn't take such drastic steps...

✦ William is the first heir to the British throne to have been born in a hospital.

✦ Windsor Castle is rumoured to be haunted by Henry VIII, Anne Boleyn and Elizabeth I.

The Queen celebrated her 90th birthday back in 2016

✦ Since there has never been an Elizabeth I of Scotland, all post boxes in Scotland bear just the crown with no initials.

✦ Technically, the Queen still owns all the sturgeon, whales and dolphins in UK waters, because of a statute in 1324.

✦ The Queen's personal fortune is estimated at around £350 million.

✦ The Queen's favourite tipple is gin and Dubonnet, while Prince Philip prefers a whisky and soda.

✦ Prince Charles is the longest serving king-in-waiting and the oldest heir to the throne in history.

All Change!

Lily's daughter is about to embark on her new life as a student… so what will she do in her empty nest?

By Julie Goodall

Next on platform two is the 8.02 to Exeter St David's, stopping at…" Lily rose from the bench, not bothering to listen to where the 8.02 would be stopping. The October chill strengthened as she moved from the relative shelter beside the building to the platform edge.

As she'd suspected, there were a lot of people commuting at that time of the morning and the number concerned her a little. On a half-hour journey, would she get a seat?

There was a bit of a scramble to board and she quickly realised that in future she must toughen up. It felt a bit *Lord Of The Flies* and she experienced a rush of relief as she slid between two bulky males pressing through the open doors. Scanning the carriage, she made her way between the two rows, her gaze settling on an empty window seat. She excused herself, tossed her rucksack onto the overhead rack then sat with a relieved sigh beside a man scrolling on his phone. He'd barely looked up as he moved his knees for her to squeeze past.

Lily looked at her watch. The train was on time, the announcement made and they pulled away. There were five stops on the way and, as they neared Exeter, the countryside morphed into a splattering of towns then finally the city.

It seemed most passengers were travelling to Exeter St David's and she waited for the guy beside her to move before collecting her rucksack and alighting with everyone else. In her pocket a printed map was folded, ready if needed, but she remembered the way from the open day and passed through the exit with her ticket, starting the ten-minute walk.

Should she ring Helena now? Every cell in her body urged her to do so and she looked at her watch once again.

Helena would probably be busy with all her new friends. Lily was sure she'd have made some by now. They'd had yesterday and the night to get acquainted and, of course, Helena had a roommate. Gosh – how Lily had dreaded this day, for so many years.

Mum! I've been accepted at Canterbury! The Politics degree. I can't believe it!"

Lily flung her arms around her daughter, excitement for her strengthening the embrace. She'd worked so hard for her exams, all the while working at the local cinema three nights a week. The extra money was intended to help support her years away because it had always been just Lily and Helena and, of course, Lily could only afford so much. The course costs were covered by her student loan, but the living expenses added up to such a lot.

"But it's four hours away," Helena went on. "Are you sure we can afford for me to live in the halls?"

"Oh Helena, what do you think I've been saving for all these years? You have no idea how proud I am of you," Lily ➔

She moved towards the edge of the platform

sniffed, surreptitiously wiping her tears. "You deserve it, and it's going to be the best years of your life so far. Make the most of every minute because… well… life has a way of getting more complicated."

"Ha. You're not kidding." Helena gently drew away and kissed her mum on the cheek. "I could never have done it without you. You've sacrificed so much for me to get this far."

Lily shook her head, not trusting herself to speak. Her daughter daintily wiped beneath her own immaculately made-up eyes, her pink nails shaped to perfection. Helena always seemed to manage everything to a level that Lily had

Lily strode into the kitchen and opened the fridge.

"This definitely calls for a celebration." She held a bottle of bubbly aloft. "I know it's only prosecco but we'll just have to close our eyes and imagine."

"I don't need to imagine," Helena laughed, collecting two glasses from the cupboard over the washing machine. "I prefer prosecco anyway. Here's to the best mum in the business."

Lily smiled.

"I don't know about that," she said, "but here's to the daughter of the century. Things will be different, of course they will, but I'm always here if you need me. I don't need to tell you that."

Now the desire to share her secret with her daughter was overwhelming

never quite achieved. She had no doubt Helena would cope with her degree years just as well.

As for herself… she'd spent the past few years dreading this. After eighteen years of the two of them, the nest would be well and truly empty. She'd spent a long time wondering how she'd cope.

"I'll come back as often as possible," Helena promised, brushing Lily's wayward blonde hair from her face. "I don't want you to feel lonely."

"You certainly won't, young lady," Lily admonished, pecking her small turned-up nose. "You'll go away and enjoy yourself. I'm a big girl now and will cope perfectly well without you." She saw Helena's gaze drop momentarily and was worried she'd gone too far. "I'll miss you, of course I will. Desperately. But you're not to worry about me. I've got my am-dram group at the theatre. This is all about you and the start of your future."

It was time to tell her, Lily thought, entering the campus and heading for the reception. The grass was damp from the night dew and she made certain to stay on the path. She'd worn trainers because it would be a long day, and on open day no one had dressed up.

Droves of students headed for the main building and Lily pulled out her phone. She'd not wanted to take anything away from Helena's first day, but now the desire to share this with her daughter was overwhelming. She'd kept this a secret for long enough.

"Mum? Everything OK? Hold on…" There was a buzz of conversation in the background and Lily felt reassured that her daughter had already made friends all the way up in Kent. "I'm just headed for class."

"Me too." Lily laughed, then held her breath. A silence followed and she waited for the penny to drop.

"You're headed for class? Mum? What d'you mean?"

Lily let the silence linger for a moment, happy to elongate the suspense.

"My class. My drama class. Exeter University accepted me for a BA in Drama. Afterwards, I intend to do my PGCE and teach."

"What?" Again there was silence and Lily failed to supress a smile. "But… how…?"

A student brushed past as Lily ascended the entrance steps. She moved to one side.

"I'm not boarding, obviously. I'll come in by train for my classes. It's only Exeter."

"What about work?" Lily heard the excitement in Helena's voice tinged with confusion.

"They've let me go part-time, flexi hours. I cashed in an ISA. I decided that you only live once. When I'm finally teaching, the increase in salary will more than make up for it."

"Mum, that's amazing! I can't believe you didn't tell me! My mum, a drama teacher! That's sick!"

"Well, I don't know if that's good or bad, but I'm hoping it's the former." Lily laughed. "Anyway, we'd best get to our classes. We don't want to be late on our first day."

"Ring me later, Mum! I want to hear all about how it went."

"Ditto." Lily laughed. "Love you, sweetheart."

"Love you too."

Lily pressed the red button on her phone but not before hearing Helena yell at her classmates, "My mum's at university!" She laughed out loud with joy.

Lily went inside the building and found where she needed to be. There was a queue and she took a seat, thinking about what it had taken to get here, what soul-searching and dredging-up of confidence to take this fork in her sometimes quite potholed road.

Until now, Helena had taken up every ounce of her energy but perhaps forty was now the new thirty? Definitely not too late to begin a new, long-awaited career.

It was Lily's time. It would be tough without Helena at home, for sure, but an empty nest needn't be the end of the world. Lily had decided she needed to be like the magpie, bringing something else in to where the space was, something shiny and new, yet not a replacement. An addition to her life.

"Can I help you?"

Lily stood and walked to the counter, thinking that, in all this, there was only one potential problem. If Helena also decided to teach as she intended to, and also did a PGCE, what a nightmare if their graduations turned out to be on the same day…

Of course, Lily knew which one she would miss. No competition. She handed over her paperwork and smiled at the receptionist. Her life as a university drama student was about to begin. (MW)

MY MAGIC MOMENT…

Aged 26, I received my first ever letter from my birth mother. I'd secretly dreamed of being a writer but her disclosure that she had been published convinced me that it wasn't the craziest idea!

Let's Make Jam

Pippa clung to summer, but Max showed her that there was a certain magic in all the seasons of the year

By Camilla Kelly

I love autumn," Max said, sniffing the rain-soaked air blissfully.

"Not me," Pippa said, looking miserably at the sky.

Thankfully they'd found a café awning to shelter under, but they hadn't been quick enough to gather up the picnic before getting drenched.

"I hate it when the weather changes."

She glanced at Nadia and Lewis – new friends she'd made since meeting Max. Nadia was tipping the rain out of the brim of her sun hat.

"Anyway," Pippa said hopefully, "summer isn't over yet. There's still some light evenings to come…"

"It's a bold attempt," Max said, "but I think you're going to have to accept it. There's plenty of other stuff we can do."

She sighed. "It won't be the same."

Summer was her favourite season. It always started so hopefully. That first-day-of-the-holidays feeling, where anything might happen, stayed with her even through countless disappointing years of record rainfall, or ant infestations, or cancelled flights.

This year summer had actually lived up to its promise. This year there was Max. And the beach, and pub gardens, and open-air movies. Long summer days that went on forever.

"I've got an idea." Max's face lit up. "Jam making!"

Max was a super-nerdy foodie. She loved that about him.

So, as he asked, she turned up at his flat a few days later with a bag of fruit, trying to ignore the early twilight that followed her there.

"Wait until you smell the jam cooking on the stove," he said, leading her into the kitchen. "If that doesn't get you loving autumn, nothing will."

Nadia and Lewis were already there, with a crate of blackberries they'd picked from hedgerows, looking very pleased with themselves.

Pippa unveiled the strawberries that she'd bought at the supermarket, the last of the season.

"Ooh, they look good," Nadia said.

"Remember when we watched the Wimbledon final with strawberries and cream?" Pippa said. "Have one. They taste just like summer."

By the time the blackberry jam had been made, all the strawberries had been eaten!

Pippa blushed. "I couldn't help myself."

To her mind, fresh fruit would always be nicer than jam.

So the jam-making session didn't go according to plan.

Max had another idea.

"We'll start a supper club," he suggested. "Pip, you can go first."

She came into the living room, where the curtains were drawn and candles were lit. A stew simmered on the stove, smelling delicious.

"OK," Max said.

"Really?" She was worried he might think it silly.

"I love spending sunny days with you. I hope we can plan a million of them."

She melted a little, feeling some of the strange tension she'd been carrying around for weeks suddenly lighten.

"Pip, I also looked forward to spending cold, frosty days with you," he said, kissing her nose.

"I know I'm clinging to summer," she blurted. "It's because it was so perfect and I'm afraid of things changing... Winter has always been a little lonely for me."

Summer was Pippa's favourite season – and this summer there was Max

Pippa had a barbecue. She stood outside for half an hour, holding an umbrella over the grill, trying to get the flame hot enough to cook something despite the drizzle. Inside, Max ordered pizza and waited for her to join them.

Max had gone back to work as a teacher now and so there were no more days when he'd meet her in the park in her lunchbreak, or walk her home after work.

"Come over to dinner at the weekend," he said, to console her. "We'll have a night in, just you and me."

She cheered at the thought. "I know what we can do."

She arrived with her arms full of sunny travel brochures.

"I thought we could pretend we're planning a dream holiday. Just for fun..."

Max put his arm around her and pulled her down to sit on the sofa.

"But if you let go of summer, we can move on to autumn – my favourite. I've been trying to share with you why. It's this," he whispered into her ear, pulling her into his comfortable warmth. "Just this."

They sat quietly, her head on his shoulder, listening to the wind outside and looking into the soft glow of the fire. She had nowhere to be but here, safe and wanted.

"I think I get it," she said. ⓜ

. . . .
MY MAGIC MOMENT...

When my friend took me horse-riding, it was a temperamental spring day, and as we came over the hill the sunlight over the moorland was breathtaking.

A Date With Destiny

Can the sudden reappearance of the boy from Nicole's past somehow throw light on her future?

By **Tara Westgate**

It's really good to see you again," Dylan said over the cafe table. "I've been thinking about school a lot recently. You were the only girl who would talk to me."

Nicole hadn't seen Dylan Anderson since their schooldays, and now she lived miles away from their home town. She'd bumped into him on the street outside her office, when she was just about to grab some lunch, and invited him to join her for a quick catch-up.

"I really liked hanging out with you," she said. "You always had something interesting to say, and you made me

I used to be a disaster, and I know it."

Back then he'd had long, greasy hair and acne, and he looked as if he'd got dressed in the dark. The present-day Dylan was smart, clear-skinned, had a decent haircut and loads more social confidence. He'd changed so much that when he'd stopped her on the street, she hadn't recognised him at first.

"Well – you've scrubbed up pretty well," she said. "What are you doing with yourself these days? You used to say you wanted to be an inventor."

"Yep. And now I am."

"Oh, wow! Have you worked out how to save the world yet? I always thought you might."

"You'll have to see for yourself – and I have to swear you to absolute secrecy"

laugh, too. It's a shame some of the other kids were so mean."

"Yeah," he said. "They were. You were great, though. You even stuck up for me when it all got a bit much, and told them to lay off. I'll never forget that. It takes a brave person to defend the class nerd."

"Oh, I wouldn't say you were a nerd, Dylan." She laughed, embarrassed.

"Really? Come on – let's be honest.

"Not quite, but I have got something new that I'd really love to show you. Are you free this evening?"

"Sure." She smiled. "What is it?"

"You wouldn't believe me if I told you. You'll have to see it for yourself – and I have to swear you to absolute secrecy.

"I know I can trust you, probably more than most people. No one knows about this so far. I don't have anyone I can ➤

absolutely trust, but I want to share it with someone."

That evening, Dylan picked her up from her office. He was just visiting for a couple of weeks, and he drove her to his luxury holiday rental on the outskirts of the city.

When they walked into the sitting room, Nicole immediately noticed six tower computers on the floor by one of the armchairs. He pointed to that chair.

"You'd better sit down, because this is going to blow your mind," he said. She took the chair, looking curiously at the array of computers. "Nicole – I've discovered a way of seeing the future."

She stared at him, speechless.

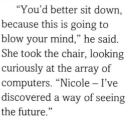

"My system is no good for big, complicated questions; the sort of things that involve a lot of people. So far, I've only got it to work on a personal level. All you can do with it is ask questions about a specific thing that you're thinking of doing, and this machine will show you the consequences of that action. It needs to be, *If I do this, what will the result be?*"

"It shows you? Do you see things?"

"Yes. It's like a film, with pictures and sound. This system is a way of seeing possible futures, because the future isn't one fixed, certain entity. What you'll see isn't guaranteed to come true, because so many things could happen to change that particular future. I don't totally understand it myself yet. I think what it shows is the most likely outcome. Do you want to give it a go?"

"Wow – yes," she said.

"All right. You need to put this on." He passed her something that looked like a

rubber swimming cap, which was covered with wires. The wires were connected to the tower computers.

Nicole trusted Dylan, completely. She wasn't worried about being safe while she was linked up to his new invention. She'd known him well enough at school to be sure that he definitely wasn't the type to hurt anyone. She pulled the cap on.

"When you're ready, just start thinking about your question – in as much detail as possible."

"OK," she said.

"Now sit back and close your eyes," Dylan instructed. "Don't suddenly open them, and don't speak. When you've seen enough and you want to come out of it, just raise your hand."

"OK," she repeated, closing her eyes.

There was one easy question right at the forefront of her mind. For the past couple of weeks she had been seeing two guys, just for casual coffees and lunches.

They were both showing signs of wanting to get more serious, so she needed to choose which one of them she was going to start properly dating, and which one to let down gently.

She set herself to think about Brandon. He was tall, dark, handsome; charming and intelligent, too. So, what would it be like if he became her significant other? For a minute or two, nothing happened, and then colours began to form behind her closed eyelids. They resolved into an image of a room. Slowly, the details became clearer and clearer. It was an expensive-looking kitchen, with a huge table and a central island unit – the type of kitchen owned by people with money to burn. There were floor-to-ceiling windows on one wall, and it was dark outside. The lights were on.

And then Nicole saw herself, as an older woman. Gosh, but this was so weird! She was wearing a skirt suit and heels. It was the sort of outfit that obviously hadn't cost peanuts. She was still slim, but she looked haggard, as if she'd been stressed

and Brandon following each other around the huge kitchen.

She was on the attack, and he kept walking away from her. He went behind the central unit, using it as a barrier between them. And now she could hear whole sentences.

"I forgave you once," she said. "How can you possibly expect me to forgive you again? You're just a cheater, and you're never going to change."

"Honestly, I swear – it was just physical. It doesn't make any difference to the way I feel about you."

Nicole didn't need to see much more, but she stayed with it, just to be sure.

Brandon was a serial womaniser. If she chose him, he'd be unfaithful, and make

"I'm going to have to go very carefully. Do you want to ask it something else?"

out for years. She was talking, but there was no sound. Her worn face showed anger and distress.

Being able to see a real, live, moving image of herself as she would look in the future… this was the strangest thing that had ever happened in her entire life. It was just bizzare.

Brandon stepped into the picture, also looking distressed. How old were they? About early forties, she reckoned. He still looked good – he'd aged better than she had. He was wearing a business suit.

It looked as if they'd been out at work, and they were meeting up at home after a long day… yes, she was sure that was the situation. There was nothing to prove it, but she could somehow sense exactly what was going on.

Nicole began to hear some individual words, just very faintly. The sound grew gradually louder. She watched herself

her miserable. They'd be rich and successful, but she wouldn't be happy. She had seen enough. She raised her hand, and the sound and picture gradually faded out.

"You can open your eyes now," Dylan said gently.

Nicole opened them. He was looking at her eagerly. "Well?" he asked.

"Wow," she said. "Just wow. It works. There is no way you could have faked that – not that I think you would, of course. It's absolutely amazing!"

"Isn't it?" he said. "It's so amazing that I doubt it's something I can ever release into the world. I'm not sure what the consequences would be."

"No." Her eyes widened. "It could cause some serious trouble."

"I think so. I'm going to have to go very carefully with it. Do you want to ask it something else?" ➜

"Yes, I do," she said eagerly, settling back in the armchair and closing her eyes once again. This time, she would think about Scott.

Nicole concentrated on him. Scott also seemed to be a really nice guy. He was a blond, super-fit outdoor type. He had a great sense of humour, and was always up for a laugh.

She'd met him when they'd both been in the audience at a stand-up comedy night. Scott had ambition, though – he was a surf instructor, and his dream was to open a chain of surf schools.

Gradually a picture began to form. This time, it was an outdoor scene. A garden, with a distant view of the sea. And there was Scott, lying asleep on a sun lounger.

He looked rough. He'd put on loads of weight, and was now a human blob. Flab hung over the top of his shorts. Empty, squashed beer cans littered the ground around the lounger.

And there she was, walking into the picture – once again, she looked stressed out and haggard. Her future self shook Scott's shoulder, with an expression of disgust on her face.

Then the sound came up, but she didn't need to hear what she was saying to know what the situation was. Scott had turned into a hopeless, lazy drunk. She got it now – what she was seeing, in both the scenes of her possible futures, was the time when she realised that her relationship with these men was over.

Nicole raised her hand, and the picture faded out.

"Do you know what I was seeing?" she asked. "Can you look too?"

"No, don't worry. I can't, and the system doesn't record anything. It's completely private."

She had a sudden thought.

"Dylan…" she began, slowly. "You've looked at your own possible futures, of course?"

"Of course," he said, smiling.

"Are you involved with anyone?"

"I'm not, no."

"Why is that?"

"Because the woman I want to spend my life with doesn't know yet that she wants to spend her life with me."

Nicole was getting a very strong intuition about all this.

"It wasn't an accident, was it? You bumping into me today?"

"I won't lie to you. No, it wasn't. I hope you'll forgive me. I tracked you down online, and found out where you worked. I'm sorry if that's too stalker-ish – I hope it isn't." He paused for a moment, looking down at his hands. When he raised his head again, he said, "You're the nicest, kindest woman I've ever met – oh, and quite possibly the most beautiful, although that's not the important thing."

"This woman you want to spend your life with," she said. "Have you asked your system about her?"

"Yes, I have."

"And did you like what you saw?"

"Very much," he answered.

They both smiled, and then Nicole said, "I've just realised that I can see the future, too. I can do it without using your system."

"You can? And what do you see?" he asked softly.

"I see a really great evening, Dylan. One I'll always remember…" Ⓜ

....

MY MAGIC MOMENT…

When I went swimming in the sea off the Isle of Mull. I was suddenly surrounded by a large colony of seals. They didn't seem to mind my being there, and I got so close to them that I could look into their eyes.

Brain Boosters SOLUTIONS

CODEWORD FROM PAGE 23
PHRASE: AMERICAN AND ISRAELI

S	U	I	T	A	B	L	E		P	A	S	T	E
	N		E		U		N		R		W		X
E	A	S	I	E	S	T		C	R	O	Q	U	E	T
F		K		M		C		O		P		N		R
F	L	I	T		H	Y	D	R	A	N	G	E	A
E		L		U		E		E		G			V
R	E	F	I	N	E	R	Y		F	A	S	C	I	A
V		U		R		Y		L		N		O		G
E	C	L	A	I	R		B	A	N	D	A	N	N	A
S		V		O		C		A		J		N	
C	O	R	I	A	N	D	E	R		P	U	T	T
E		O		L		O		Z		R		L	
N	A	T	A	L	I	E		S	P	E	C	I	F	Y
C		O		E		S		S		A		N	
E	R	R	E	D		T	H	E	O	L	O	G	Y

KRISS KROSS FROM PAGE 131

	S	U	P	P	L	E		D	
	A		A		A	O		O	
Q		N	V		P	S	Y	C	H	E
U	N	S	C	R	E	W		E	K	L
A		T		M		L			I
R	E	T	I	C	E	N	T		R	T
T		O		N			T	O	P	E
E	M	A	N	A	T	E		S	O
T		X		R		M	U	S	T	Y
	I		D			P		O
	S	N	O	W	C	A	P		U
		U			E	A	R	N
	S	C	O	R	C	H	E	R		G

MISSING LINK FROM PAGE 61
ACROSS: 1 Cash 3 Coconut 8 Alarm 9 Idiot 10 Log 12 Spark 14 Pound 16 Straw 20 Wheel 22 Fox 24 Large 25 Novel 27 Witness 28 Mean
DOWN: 1 Candle 2 Sea 3 Combat 4 Cricket 5 Nail 6 Tattoo 7 Bass 11 Good 13 Half 15 Nowhere 17 Pillow 18 Tennis 19 Oxygen 21 Live 23 Fret 26 Lie
SHADED WORD: CHILLI

MISSING LINK FROM PAGE 75
ACROSS: 1 Fall 3 Tropical 8 Ready 9 Panel 11 Clerk 12 Harvest 14 Fast 16 Peer 20 Optical 22 Blown 24 Drama 26 Going 27 Identity 28 Knee
DOWN: 1 French 2 Large 4 Rhythm 5 Paper 6 Can 7 Basket 10 Late 13 Eye 15 Art 16 Public 17 Load 18 Flight 19 Engine 21 Coast 23 Organ 25 Awe
SHADED WORD: TEAPOT

SUDOKU 1 FROM PAGE 115

4	6	1	2	9	7	3	5	8
8	3	7	5	4	1	2	9	6
9	2	5	3	6	8	7	4	1
3	8	2	9	1	5	6	7	4
6	1	4	7	8	2	5	3	9
5	7	9	6	3	4	1	8	2
1	9	3	4	5	6	8	2	7
7	4	8	1	2	3	9	6	5
2	5	6	8	7	9	4	1	3

SUDOKU 2 FROM PAGE 115

9	1	7	5	2	6	4	8	3
2	8	4	3	7	1	9	5	6
6	5	3	8	4	9	2	1	7
4	3	1	7	6	5	8	9	2
7	6	2	4	9	8	5	3	1
5	9	8	1	3	2	6	7	4
3	4	9	2	8	7	1	6	5
1	2	6	9	5	3	7	4	8
8	7	5	6	1	4	3	2	9

WORD WHEEL FROM PAGE 115 The nine-letter word is LONGEVITY

Simply The Best

All our lives, my sister had always won. But the rules were completely different in this game

By Jo Styles

As soon as my sister, Zoe, drove up to her house, she checked my bump. "Does he like crisps? You are on bag number two."

"I had a craving." I shoved the packet into my pocket. "Bring the bags in, will you? My back's killing me."

Slowly, I extricated myself from the car. I trundled flat-footedly to the front door while Zoe quickly grabbed a pile of carriers from the boot. I wished shopping had left me with so much energy.

"Are you sure about eating all this weird stuff, Jess? Do you really think it'll induce labour? You're going to get terrible indigestion."

"I get that anyway, and heartburn. I need to get this baby out of me… and I do want to be first!"

We'd competed our whole lives. Only my sister – the more gifted at running, swimming and every academic subject going – had won every time.

She'd gone to uni first, started a career first and married first. Now I'd trounced her, I'd have the first baby.

"Don't forget to ring Mum and Dad as soon as anything happens. Take photos of the baby as soon as you can, too," I told her. I intended to make sure there'd be a hundred pictures of my little one winging back and forth amongst our family.

In Zoe's lounge, after doing a little waitress service, she perched on the edge of a chair.

Chewing on canned pineapple – which is supposed to work – I frowned.

"You're making me feel like a monkey in the zoo, watching me like that." I

swallowed down another chunk. "I'll have curry for lunch. Spicy food sometimes helps. I did a ton of research about speeding things along. It's castor oil next. Just a bit."

"Oh, tasty. I'll get that for you, shall I?"

While she was busy in the kitchen, I sipped at a cup of tea and stared at a gold trophy on the sideboard. Jessica had entered – and won – a fun-run last year. I'd managed to come in about ninety-fourth. I stared down at my bump.

"You do realise you passed the finishing line two weeks ago, don't you? You should be on a podium by now holding a bunch of flowers –"

From the kitchen came a loud crash.

"Did you drop the bottle, butterfingers?" I called. I pushed myself out of my chair and waddled through the house.

Castor oil lay in a circle of glass on the tiles. My sister stood over the greasy mess. "Sorry," Zoe all but gasped.

As soon as she added a groan, I realised what was happening.

"You're joking. That's so unfair."

She wrapped both hands around her own big, wide belly.

"Maybe it's gas?" Her wild, panicked eyes met mine. "I didn't want to be first, honest. I wanted to hear all your birthing anecdotes. I wanted you to tell me about your cursing in the delivery room… and what it all really felt like." She flung out a hand and caught hold of mine. "I'm scared, Jess. I'm really, really scared."

With my own baby hanging about for so long, it seemed that hers had just caught up. She was having contractions, so I'd lose… yet again.

I breathed for a moment. I learned how in antenatal classes. *In for five, out for five, and relax. It's going to be all right.* It's a perfectly natural process… always coming in second. I'd had this down to a T.

"You're brilliant, Zoe." I beamed. "You're a star. You'll ace this."

She blinked at my familiar words. I said them before all her victories.

Tears glistened in her eyes.

"You're the best sister ever."

Hang on a sec. She's right, I thought. *I am. I've endured. I've actually even bloomed. I'm kind and selfless – no matter what.*

"I'll look after you." I soothed. "I'll ring round and alert everybody, then we'll get your stuff and get you to the hospital."

She clutched at my hand harder still.

"Well, I will – once you stop cutting off my circulation."

"I don't want to do this without you, Jess," she gasped.

"You won't have to, I'm here."

I'm sure I heard a crowd applaud and roar out their approval. Honestly, sometimes it's greatest feeling in the world being number two. **MW**

The Very Talented Man

He was gorgeous and artistic, too – if only this lovely
stranger would show some interest in Rosie…

By Ginny Swart

Rosie looked around the crowded coffee shop and with relief, spotted a free table in the corner. She plopped gratefully into the chair, dumping her enormous career-girl bag on the floor at her feet.

She flipped open a magazine and sat back to enjoy a cappuccino and chocolate brownie, a treat she felt she deserved after a whole afternoon of designing a website.

"Is this seat taken?"

She gazed up at the best-looking man she'd seen in weeks. No, make that months. Tall, tanned and blue-eyed, with a dimple in his chin.

"No, it's not."

the old man at the opposite table as his subject, instead of herself. His pencil moved confidently across the page, outlining the hunched shoulders and baggy jacket and building up the shadows in quick, sharp lines.

She craned her neck to look closer, and caught his eye as she did so.

"That's really good," she offered. "It looks just like him."

"You think so?" He held it out at a distance, considering. "I'm not sure about his head, I think I've made it too long. And his ears aren't right…"

"He's perfect!" she insisted. "You're incredibly talented."

"That's kind of you." He was quietly pleased, she could see. "I usually paint in

His pencil moved confidently, building up the shadows in quick, sharp lines

He sat down with his espresso, gave her a polite smile and pulled a small sketch book from his leather briefcase. He proceeded to make a speedy, very recognisable drawing of someone sitting nearby.

Rosie was fascinated – she'd never watched an artist at work. And she felt a bit slighted that he should have chosen

oils but I like to sketch interesting people whenever I can, to use later. That guy has wonderful cheekbones."

So have I, thought Rosie enviously. *Why not ask me to model for you? What's so amazingly interesting about that old bloke?*

But Blue Eyes kept staring at his drawing, changed the angle of the ears in

a few strokes and signed his name with a flourish.

"There," he said, satisfied. "Got him."

He closed his sketchbook with a snap and bent to replace it in his brief case but as he did so he bumped the edge of the small table. Clumsily trying to save the plate, he sent Rosie's cappuccino flying, and hot coffee shot out across the table onto her magazine and cascaded down onto the floor – as well as her shoes.

Blue Eyes grabbed a handful of paper serviettes from the holder and tried to mop up the spillage – rather ineffectually.

"I'm terribly sorry," he apologised, dabbing the magazine with a paper napkin but dropping his sketch book and pencil to the floor at the same time. "Oh heck, I'm so darned clumsy."

Rosie smiled forgivingly. Even though her chocolate brownie was a mass of wet crumbs under the table.

"No worries."

"I've ruined your magazine. Let me buy you a new one."

"No." She grinned, "Rather than a ➤

new glossy I'd like that little drawing you've just done instead. I've never owned an original work of art."

"This? But it's no work of art, it's just a quick sketch."

"I know, but it's so good. And it will remind me of you. I'm Rosie, by the way."

She smiled up at him prettily, hoping he'd take this opportunity which she'd practically thrown at his face and introduce himself. And take it from there, as any red-blooded man would.

But he frowned slightly, then said, "Well, OK." and carefully tore out the sketch and handed it to her.

"Fair enough. If you think that's a fair swap! Thanks."

Rosie watched him leave the café, his briefcase swinging.

I wonder what he does for a living, she thought. *He doesn't look like an artist in that suit, but the sketch is great. Maybe I'll have it framed.*

She needed to report this encounter with the talented Mr Gorgeous to her best mate Jane as soon as possible. On a scale of one to ten, this guy was a definite nine. Too bad he didn't have the self-confidence to ask her for a date.

She picked up her bag and scrabbled through it to find her phone – which was when she realised it was missing. Along with her leather purse.

Instantly, cold realisation set in. Damn! So sketching wasn't Mr Gorgeous's only talent. She sat frozen with rage. Knocking over her coffee had been nothing but a clever diversion – and she'd completely fallen for it.

She considered reporting the incident, and sighed. The thief was long gone and she guessed what had occurred would be classed as petty crime.

Petty crime! Major disaster, more like, Rosie thought indignantly. Even though her purse had been practically empty of cash, it was her credit cards and store cards she was furious about. Replacing them would mean hours on the phone and forms to fill in! A complete waste of her precious spare time!

Well, be grateful that's all he took." comforted Jane later. "At least he didn't get your laptop."

"Only because it would have been too difficult to tuck up his sleeve!"

"Let's see that sketch." Jane looked at it in admiration. "That's very good. Maybe one day he'll be famous and this will be worth a fortune."

"You think? Portrait of an unknown man by an unknown artist?"

"Hang on," said Jane, "He's signed it!"

They both peered at the signature, an artistic scribble in the corner.

"Can't make that out." said Rosie in disgust. "It could be a Mark. Or a Mike. It's all curls and wiggles. He just wrote that to fool me."

"No, I don't think so. Most artists sign their work automatically, without thinking about it. I bet this is his real name, if we could only read it."

But they couldn't, and Rosie spent the next hour on the phone angrily cancelling her credit cards. And that, she hoped, was the end of an unpleasant experience.

A week later Rosie was walking past the annual art-in-the-park exhibition and stopped in front of a striking portrait of an old man.

It was the old man from the café – but this time he was painted in colourful oils, wearing some sort of medieval costume. He smiled out of the frame with a twinkle in his eye. It looked almost like one of those Old Masters and was exactly the sort of picture she would have liked to buy, if she could afford it.

The signature was the same

"And that's such a noble old face," she continued. "He looks almost regal. I can't imagine someone like him ever drinking a cappuccino, or using a mobile phone, can you? Although I'm sure he does. They're such incredibly useful things, aren't they, mobiles?"

Mike Hodges made a choking sound and went bright red. He seemed rooted to the spot and Rosie felt almost sorry for him. He looked young and vulnerable and she suddenly realised that if she called the police, his future as an artist would look pretty bleak.

She made a quick decision. Everyone deserved a second chance, and it really was a beautiful picture. It would look perfect above her fireplace.

"Worth a fortune? A portrait of an unknown man by an unknown artist?"

indecipherable whirl of circles.

"Wonderful, isn't it?" smiled the lady in charge. "He's an amateur but so talented. The critics are predicting a great future for him."

"Who's the artist?"

"Mike Hodges. He's a member of our art group. Oh, there he is now." She waved at the tall figure loping towards them. "Mike! You have a fan!"

Same blue eyes, same dimpled chin.

He smiled at Rosie in modest acknowledgement.

"Glad you like it."

He obviously doesn't recognise me, she thought. *Not surprising, he hardly looked at my face – he was too busy checking out my bag.*

"I think you're really talented," she gushed. "You have… such clever fingers."

Something clicked in his mind and his face stiffened.

"How kind of you to give me this picture, Mike," she said sweetly. "I'll hang it in my living room and every time I look at it, I'll remember you."

She tried not to sound too threatening but he got the message.

"I'm delighted that you'll accept it," he said quickly, lifting it down and removing the price tag which – Rosie was happy to see – was way more than she could ever have afforded. And a great deal more than her old mobile had cost.

Yes – a pretty fair swap, she thought, all things considered. 🅜🅦

The Perfect Present

Every family has one – a person who is absolutely impossible to please when it comes to buying a gift

By Patsy Collins

A small reward for you," Lin said as she handed Harold a generous glass of sherry.

"I thought we were saving this for Christmas? Not that I'm complaining."

"It feels as though Christmas is coming early. We're doing really well with the presents this year. The ones I've bought are already wrapped, and I've just had an email to say everything I've bought on the internet has been despatched, so I'm feeling quite festive."

"Great!" said Harold, who hated to see his wife stressed out over the Christmas shopping. He hated her to worry *almost* as much as he hated getting involved to help them. The problem was that he always had his hands full and had to pull off his gloves and search through his pockets and he always dropped things and then his shopping got mixed up.

He wouldn't remember whether he'd got everything and he'd go back for a few things just in case. Then he'd spot the perfect present for someone whom he'd just bought a gift for. That had been the first thing he'd seen that was remotely suitable. So, he bought the perfect thing, but then realised that meant he'd spent more on one child than the others so bought more to even things up.

Then he'd come out and the tin rattlers had changed shifts and in the crush at the tills he'd lost the stickers showing he'd

"I just need something to wrap – and a receipt so she can bring it back"

with the shopping himself. He detested battling through packed, overheated shops that blasted Christmas songs at him. He became irritated at being constantly accosted by excessively jolly people in red who waved charity collecting tins at him.

He didn't mind giving some change; there were plenty of people, animals too, in need of food or shelter and he wanted given, so he'd had to juggle even more bags as he searched for change and hoped the car park ticket hadn't expired yet.

There was no need to get worked up, he remembered. Luckily this year, Lin had got everything done while he worked overtime to pay for it and he was spared the dreaded visit to the shopping centre. Harold took another sip of his sherry ➔

and sighed with enormous satisfaction.

Lin continued, "I am pleased with how organised I've been. I've even made a cake and put a couple of batches of mince pies into the freezer."

"Marvellous!" said Harold, who was very partial to home-made Christmas cake and mince pies.

"There's just one gift left to buy," Lin said in a carefully casual tone. "Maybe you could get it while I put up the

decorations, make brandy butter and take the neighbours' cards round?" She gave a him hopeful smile.

It sounded such a reasonable request. It probably *was* a reasonable request, yet still it filled him with dread. He gulped.

"Er, is this final gift for my mother?"

"Yes it is, actually." Lin's tone was now slightly more careful and a bit less casual, but she kept her hopeful smile in place.

He was pretty sure he knew the answer to his next question, but he asked it anyway… "Have you thought of something suitable?"

If she, or anyone else, had then it would be a first. His daughter had asked for suggestions just a few days ago.

"Gran's already got anything that would be suitable," Julie complained. "Every time I have an idea, I visit Gran and see her wearing or using whatever I've thought of."

Harold had agreed. "Mum buys whatever she wants herself. I wish she'd just tell us what she'd like, but she says it's no fun unless it's a surprise."

Finding a suitable gift for Harold's mum was a problem for the whole family. Harold's dad often joked, during one of the regular family discussions on the subject, that he just went into the first clothes shop he found and asked for anything they had for the price he wanted to pay.

"They ask what type of garment and I say it doesn't matter, they ask what size and colour, I say that doesn't matter, I just need something to wrap and a receipt so she can bring it back and change it. You definitely need to keep the receipt whatever it is – money up in smoke otherwise."

Harold's brother confessed that he usually bought her present in a charity shop.

"Why not? It'll end up there anyway," he said defiantly.

"Or she'll give it to someone else to *look after it* for her," Lin had remarked.

Lin had sometimes picked gifts her sister-in-law would like, as she knew her birthday was in January. Harold's mother often recycled unwanted Christmas gifts by re-wrapping them in birthday paper and giving them as an extra present to her daughter.

Remembering these remarks was no help to Harold. He considered buying gift vouchers, but he couldn't do it. His mum always loved to receive beautifully wrapped gifts and to open them after Christmas lunch. She said it was so exciting to see what was inside and she appreciated the trouble people had gone to – even if she never, ever kept whatever item she was given.

She was always generous and thoughtful when she bought gifts too. He had to buy her something.

He thought of really carrying through his dad's idea of getting anything at all plus a receipt, but all the clothing shops were so busy he couldn't face going in for something he knew wasn't right.

The charity shop wasn't so busy; maybe he could get something to unwrap and give her vouchers too?

That might have been acceptable, but there was nothing remotely suitable for Mum. He did find a vase in the exact colour of the curtains his daughter had just made for her new flat, so he bought that for her. He also bought a book he thought his dad would like, and told the

Concerned people were eager to call an ambulance to get him checked over, or give him hot sweet tea for shock, or make him go into shops and lie down, or give him a lift home. Harold hadn't realised there were so many things that could be done for someone who'd fallen over, nor that there were so many kind people willing to do them.

He didn't want the fuss though, it was worse than getting through the tills while harassed assistants asked if he wanted batteries and insurance and gift wrap.

"I'm going to my daughter's flat just over there," he said escaping all but one of the good Samaritans. That young man insisted on walking with him.

"I don't want to inconvenience you,"

He thought it best to check with someone who hadn't just banged their head

cashier there was no need for change.

"That's very generous of you, sir," she said, taking the note that Harold only then realised was larger than the one he'd meant to offer. Oh well – that'd see someone hungry got a good meal or two, he didn't begrudge it.

When he walked down the street and saw someone with a tin for the same charity, Harold decided he'd done enough. Instead of wrestling with gloves and bags he crossed the street to avoid the girl. At least, he tried to. Instead, he tripped over the kerb and fell, banging his head.

He saw stars for a few seconds and all the thoughts about Mum's present seemed to be circling around in his head before people rushed to see if he was hurt.

After a moment to think about it, he realised he wasn't. Better yet, the red vase was unbroken… and better still, he'd had a very bright idea about Mum's present.

Harold said. "You must have Christmas shopping to do?"

"No problem. My family are going away for Christmas so I gave them their presents of foreign currency for spending money last week, and haven't any shopping left to do."

Harold guessed his daughter wouldn't mind if he arrived bearing a gift and a kind, attractive young man. On the way, after admitting the flat wasn't quite as close as he'd implied, he told the man about his idea for Mum's gift. He thought it was best to check with someone who hadn't just banged their head.

"That's brilliant!" the man said.

The man, Martin, drank a cup of tea with Harold and his daughter. Harold's hands didn't shake, his vision wasn't blurred, nothing hurt and he hadn't been knocked out so Julie and Martin ➜

decided he was fit to continue with the shopping. Martin left Julie his phone number and Harold left the vase.

Harold bought his mum's gift and then went home.

"Any luck?" Lin asked.

"Yes. What do you think of this?" He showed her the contents of his very large carrier bag.

"Oh, Harold! That's a funny thing to give anyone for Christmas."

"Oh." Harold had been so sure that it was a good idea.

"I don't know, though – I think your mum will like it. Yes, I'm sure she will. I was thinking, while you were out, that the gifts she buys us might be a clue to what she'd like herself. She often gets things that are bright and shiny."

"That's true, and at least we've got something to wrap, and I've kept the receipt. When I explained what it was for, the man promised our money back if she didn't want it."

"That's OK, then." Lin laughed. "And at least she won't say she's already got one!"

On Christmas Eve, Julie rang to ask if she could bring a guest for lunch. "That nice young man Martin who helped you when you fell."

"Of course, I'd be delighted to see him again," Harold said after checking with Lin that there was enough food.

"You never told me what you got for Gran, and Martin won't say anything. Is it a surprise?"

"Yes, I think your gran will be surprised." He smiled to himself. Mum would be happy to be surprised and she'd love the pretty wrapping paper and gorgeous red velvet bow Lin had used. It wouldn't matter really if she thought the present was odd and asked to exchange it.

Harold's brother was the first to arrive at the house on Christmas Day.

"Keep the receipt for Mum's present, did you?" he asked.

Harold said that he had.

"Good man. No one wants to see their money going up in smoke!"

Harold laughed, only a little nervously.

"Heard there's a new charity shop in town. I hope whatever you've bought your mother doesn't end up there," Harold's brother-in-law said when he arrived.

"That's not very likely," Harold said. Impossible, in fact; the seller would be the

What always came next? *Oh, I'll save it for later* or *it's too nice to use...*

only person who could take Mum's gift off his hands if she didn't like it.

"Come on, I bet you she's got rid of whatever it is by Boxing Day."

Harold didn't risk taking the bet.

Mum was polite about all her gifts but there was, as usual, a general feeling that no one had yet got it quite right.

She said the gloves from Julie were nice, but didn't take them out of the Cellophane. She praised the boots her husband had bought, but didn't remove the tag that held them together so she could try them on. She said the whisky Harold's brother bought would keep her warm, but didn't take off the top so she could take a sniff.

Harold handed over his gift.

"Good gracious, what a big box and so beautifully wrapped! Thank you, Harold –and you too, Lin."

Mum carefully removed the paper and bow Lin had used to make it look pretty.

"Well, that's certainly a surprise!" Mum said after a pause.

Harold winked at Lin. Everyone leaned forward, trying to see what was inside.

"I've never had anything like this before," Mum said.

Harold grinned at Lin.

There was a pause. Harold knew what everyone expected would come next. *Oh, I'll save it for later* or *It's too nice to use* or gently putting it to one side and a glance to see if there might still be a gift in someone's hand or under the tree that would actually be what she wanted.

Mum did put the gift to one side, and she did look round, but no one was holding out a gift and there was nothing under the tree.

"Oh, I almost forgot." Martin took a small gift from his pocket. "This is for you."

"That's very kind, young man. Especially as you don't even know me."

"Your son and granddaughter have spoken of you in such a way that I feel as though I do."

Mum removed the ribbon, remarking on the lovely colour. She opened the package to reveal a box of matches.

"Oh, how clever! That's exactly what I wanted. The perfect gift! Thank you."

Some of the assembled crowd looked as though they thought she was overdoing it. Some looked puzzled, one pointed out she didn't smoke or have a gas cooker.

"Exactly, and neither do Harold or Lin, which is why I so needed the matches."

Harold's smile was now a beaming grin.

"Harold and Lin," Mum said. "Would you mind very much if your lovely gift was gone by Boxing Day? I'd so like us to use it now and share it with everyone."

Harold tried to say that was fine, but was interrupted by his brother and Julie both demanding to know what it was.

"Surely you all know? No? Well, you'll get a bright, shiny surprise too then, when Harold's money goes up in smoke.

"Julie, pass me those lovely gloves you gave me, dear; I think I'll need them." She turned to Harold's brother. "The whisky you bought – put it in the beautiful hip flask your dad gave me last year and that I gave Harold to, er, look after for me. And the boots you gave me this year," she told her husband, "now would be a fine time to try them."

Although bemused, her family scurried around complying with her requests. Harold smiled at the sparkle in their eyes. Partly it was anticipation of Mum's shiny surprise, but he guessed they'd also be happy to realise their own gifts for Mum hadn't been wrong at all – it had just needed the right circumstances for them to be useful.

Once fully equipped with all her other gifts, Harold's mum and the rest of the family went out into the garden… to watch the dazzling display from Harold and Lin's gift of fireworks. Ⓜ️Ⓦ️

....

MY MAGIC MOMENT...

I was onboard a ship sailing out of Stockholm when Gary, my partner of eleven years, produced a diamond ring. It took me a moment to realise he hadn't found some lost property, but was proposing.

Round Robin

Emma's annual chronicle of how the other half live ends on an unexpected note that changes everything...

By Jan Snook

"More cards!" Suzie called to her husband as she picked up the post from the mat.

Tim came into the hall, where Suzie was still examining the envelopes.

"I think I need a coffee before I tackle this one," she groaned. "It's from Emma!"

"You sit down, I'll make the coffee," Tim said with a wry smile. "Unless Emma's completely changed her spots you'll need sustenance!"

Suzie slit open the handful of envelopes, smiling as she set the colourful collection of robins, Christmas trees and snow scenes

But Suzie wasn't listening, she was reading, and the only sounds for the next few minutes were her irritated exclamations – *Oh, really! For pity's sake! Did I honestly need to know that? Oh, not again…!*

When she had at last finished, Tim looked at her expectantly.

"Do you want to read it?" Suzie asked, still sounding cross.

Tim pulled a face.

"Could you, you know, just give me the edited highlights? Please?"

Suzie narrowed her eyes.

"Right. It's chronological, OK?" She skimmed a few lines, then said, "January, they went ski-ing (she put on a high sugary

"Then, yes, February found them golfing in Madeira to escape the ghastly weather"

on the mantelpiece. Then she took a deep breath and slid the thick wodge of paper out of Emma's large, embossed and expensive card.

"It's even longer than usual," she sighed, as Tim came in with a tray and they both sat down. "Oh for Heaven's sake! Why does she do it? Six closely typed pages!"

"It's just a boast in the post," Tim said reasonably, "she's got nothing else to do, after all. Don't get upset over it."

voice) 'to the sweet little chalet we found last year in the French Alps, just right for the two of us!' I bet that cost an arm and a leg. Then, let's see, oh yes, February found them golfing in Madeira *to escape the ghastly British weather – it's so dreary.* Dah-di-dah-di-dah… oh dear, in March and April they were *completely housebound* because they were having a new kitchen put in…"

"I thought they were having a new kitchen only a couple of years ago, weren't they?" Tim asked, looking astonished.

"I think it was four or five, actually. It was a swimming pool being built two years ago. Anyway, in July they managed a few perfect days in Rome. And all of this, I'd have you know, between running the WI, being on the parish council, being a school governor and…"

"Hang on," Tim interrupted, "a school governor? Emma? What does she know about kids?"

Suzie shrugged. "Nothing, as far as I know… Oh, she does have Claudia, of course, her god-daughter… oh, listen to this: *Claudia has a new boyfriend (wedding bells looming!) and he almost got promoted to assistant branch manager with the bank, so he must be doing well.*

"I'm sorry, but why does she think I want to hear about jobs that people I don't know didn't quite get?" Suzie turned to the next page and frowned. "Oh. They were supposed to be going on a cruise over Christmas, but it's been cancelled, and of course all the 'really good' hotels are all booked up, so they're at home by themselves. That's a bit sad."

"Don't they have brothers and sisters they could go to?"

"No. They're both only children – →

which must be rather lonely, mustn't it? I mean, I can't imagine not having family to talk to, particularly when things get… difficult. But I'd feel a bit more sympathetic if she hadn't just told me the million and one ways they'd found to enjoy themselves the rest of the year," Suzie added.

"Oh dear, I know I'm being mean. We get on really well when we're face to face. I love her dearly, I really do. But something happens to Emma when she puts pen to paper…"

She looked apologetically at Tim. He was looking miserable.

"Things have been rather difficult, haven't they?" he said. "I'm sorry, if I hadn't taken early retirement we'd have been a bit better off, love. Maybe another year we'll be able to go away for Christmas."

Suzie looked horrified.

"I didn't mean that! I like being at home for Christmas, you know I do. I love all the preparation and the decorations and the smell of the Christmas tree and the house full of our children and grandchildren and your cousins. Even if it is a bit of a squash!

"Anyway your health is far more important than a bit of extra money. And we have more time together, which is lovely."

"Yes, but wouldn't you like to go away and be spoilt one year?" he persisted, still downcast. "You know, have everything done for you? Just sit sipping champagne while someone else gets the dinner?"

"No!" Suzie said stoutly. "I'd hate to be away at Christmas in some tastefully decorated hotel, with no lovingly preserved cotton wool snowmen, made by the children when they were still at play group. It would seem terribly… *sterile* somehow."

"That's a bit harsh," Tim protested, smiling at last. "How many of us will there be this year?"

"Well, counting us… and Freddie's bringing his girlfriend, remember… fifteen," Suzie said with a bit of a gulp, counting on her fingers. "Though that includes the baby, so he doesn't really count."

"So, fourteen round the table," Tim said thoughtfully. "Could we make room for another two, d'you think?"

"But… we can't invite Emma and Julian," Suzie said, looking at him aghast. "Is that what you mean? They'd hate it. They're used to really civilised Christmases, they have a properly co-ordinated tree, and Harrods crackers and… I don't actually know what else but it's all very smart."

"But maybe not very jolly? With just the two of them?" Tim said tentatively. "Invite them. They can always say no."

But they said yes. "They sounded quite enthusiastic, actually," Suzie reported in amazement.

"And then Emma asked who was going to be here, and what they liked and didn't like and so on. Oh I'm desperately afraid that she might be going to buy lots of presents. You know what she's like…

I did tell her that we only do small things for the adults, and that she shouldn't bring any presents at all, but somehow I don't imagine she's going to comply…"

"Well that's up to her," Tim said comfortably. "It'll all be fine."

All the same, Suzie was pleased that her daughters had brought presents for Emma and Julian.

"It's just a token," Andrea said, as she put a lumpy parcel under the tree.

"Mine's tiny." Her youngest, Chloe, nodded, putting a long box next to Andrea's.

"Oh you are kind, both of you," Suzie said, relieved. "But what's that?" she asked as they both added more little presents.

"Oh, they're just from the children," Chloe said. "They wanted to join in. Actually, I hope Edwin doesn't say anything

later by Emma and Julian, the house was full to bursting. There was already a mountain of presents under the flamboyantly decorated tree, and an avalanche looked imminent – helped along by inquisitive little hands.

Julian was carrying bottles of champagne, and Emma was – predictably – laden down with yet more presents, which the children were looking at, round-eyed. She was also extremely elegantly dressed: a vision of sophistication amid the riot of Christmas jumpers the rest of them were wearing. Suzie just hoped she didn't get within range of any chocolatey fingers.

Suzie could suddenly see their family Christmas through new eyes. The clamour and colour and crowdedness of it all, but most of all the sheer noise.

"It's just a token," Andrea said, as she placed a lumpy parcel under the tree

tactless – I explained to him that Emma and Julian were coming, and that they didn't have any children or brothers and sisters, and he was appalled at the idea of someone having no family, as only a four-year-old can be. I'm afraid he's made them a cotton wool snowman to hang on their tree… not what they're used to, I'm sure!"

The family had all arrived early "to help". Although since that involved the house suddenly having four very excited children running around and four of the adults squeezing into the tiny kitchen, and baby Finn – looking very festive in a red Babygro with matching Santa hat – being passed round like a good-natured parcel, Suzie did wonder whether "help" was quite the right word.

By the time Tim's cousins, Judith and Graham, arrived, followed a few moments

"Can I do anything to help?" Emma asked a little while later, standing in the kitchen doorway. "I'm sorry, you're so busy and I'm doing nothing…"

Suzie wiped her hands on the garish Christmas apron, aware that her face was damp with perspiration from the steaming pudding, and gazed at her immaculately presented friend.

"Are you and Julian OK?" she asked. "I'm sorry about all the noise and the… crush. It must be the absolute opposite of Christmas on a cruise… what a shame it was cancelled."

Perhaps it was the champagne, but Emma started to giggle.

"It's not… not much like a cruise," she admitted. "I mean, Tim's just explained to Barney – did you say he was three? – about mistletoe, so I was dragged underneath it and kissed – quite forcibly, actually!" ➡

Julian is being initiated in the construction techniques of a rather complicated Lego model, your granddaughter has analysed my make-up in surprising and not altogether flattering detail, and I was asked to go out and run races in the garden… where I managed to ladder my tights."

"So not really like a cruise at all, then," Suzie said, and they both got such a fit of giggles that by the time Tim came into the kitchen to refill their glasses, tears were rolling down their faces.

"What on earth's going on in here?" he asked. "We can hardly hear ourselves speak in the other room, the

"Well you did really well – they're all thrilled. But next year you must promise not to buy such big presents," Suzie said sternly.

"Next year?" Emma said.

"What am I saying?" Suzie said, suddenly embarrassed. "You won't want to come next year. You'll be sunning yourselves on a Caribbean cruise, without sprout marks on your beautiful dress, and candy canes dangling from your ears – I suppose that was Jemima? – or laddering your tights running races… Oh dear!" She caught sight of what looked remarkably like dribble on Emma's shoulder. "You haven't been

Baby Finn, wearing a Santa hat, was being passed around like a good-natured parcel

racket you two are making!" He peeked under the foil covering the turkey. "This looks good. Should I be carving yet?"

Christmas lunch was a very jolly affair. The children laughed uproariously at the cracker jokes, only one paper hat fell into the gravy, the pudding was impressively alight and poor Emma was hit by a flying sprout which Edwin had had difficulty cutting.

Presents followed, and Suzie was right – Emma and Tim had brought everyone rather extravagant presents.

"I had help from the lady in the toy shop," Emma confessed to Suzie and Judith, as they sat drinking coffee while the men washed up and the grandchildren were taken for a very necessary walk. "I don't know when I last bought a present for children of this age – probably not since yours were little, Suzie. I had such fun!"

holding the baby, have you?"

Emma beamed. "I have! I was allowed a lovely long cuddle! I don't know when I last held a baby. You're so lucky having grandchildren, Suzie. And children, of course. They're all great. We've had an absolutely wonderful day."

She beamed again at the two other women. "I honestly haven't enjoyed Christmas this much since I was a child. And if there's any possibility that you'd invite us for Christmas again next year," she added, going slightly pink, "well, I know we'd both jump at the chance." **MW**

....

MY MAGIC MOMENT…

We moved from hot Venezuela to New England when I was seven. I woke up one morning to see my first ever snow – deep and sparkling against a brilliant blue sky. Unforgettable!